Dedicated to all my beloved cats,
who made me realize that every
creature is a whole world.
And to all the exploited animals
out there – I'll never stop trying
to change the world for you.

SIMPLE HAPPY KITCHEN

KITCHEN

AN ILLUSTRATED GUIDE FOR YOUR PLANT-BASED LIFE

MIKI MOTTES

Nutritional consultant: Tal Porat BSc nutrition

Simple Happy Kitchen, LLC.
www.simplehappykitchen.com
hello@simplehappykitchen.com

The book and its merchandise are available at special discounts when purchased in bulk for premiums and sales promotions as well as for fundraising or educational use. For details, contact us at hello@simplehappykitchen.com.

This book does not replace any nutritional, medical or health advice. Readers should seek their own professional counsel for any medical condition before starting or altering any dietary plan.

Every effort has been made to trace the copyright holders of materials quoted in this book. If application is made in writing to the publisher, any omissions will be included in future editions.

Printed in China.

First Edition.

ISBN 978-965-90010-0-2 (English Hardcover)
ISBN 978-965-90010-1-9 (English eBook)
ISBN 978-965-90010-4-0 (English Paperback)

OH, CREDITS!

Creator, designer and illustrator: Miki Mottes
Project manager: Ziv Meltzer
Nutritional consultant: Tal Porat BSc nutrition
Scientific editor: Kerem Avital BSc nutrition
Editor: Kerry Nenn
Logo designer: Oren Fait
Back cover blurb: Ronnie Beck
Head of lettuce: Yael Melzer

Special thanks to:

Oren Fait, Gal Mamalya, Plant Based News – Robbie Lockie, The Humane
League – John Oberg, Meatless Monday, Iron Manager, Kickstarter – Michael
Stewart, Vegan Food&Living, Livekindly, Dr. Michael Greger M.D., Peta, Jeff
Rosenberg, Anonymous for Animal Rights, Veganuary, Vegan Street, FFAC, Viva!,
Animals Australia, Ori Shavit, Purposeful Films, The Vegan Society, Eco Vegan
Gal, Freedom Farm, Voiceless, Miriam Sorrell, Viva Glam Magazine, Vega, The
Vegan Community, World Of Vegan, Vegan Huggs, Omer Matityahu, Amanda
Victoria, GoVegan World, The Lotus and the Artichoke, Vegan Green Planet,
VeganVultures, Vegan Strategist, Vegan Friendly, VegPlanet Magazine, Animal
Watch, The Vegan Voice, Maayan Cohen, Nimrod Back, Maya Alkulumbre,
Noa Ehrmann, Esther the Wonder Pig, Ludwik guinea pig and dozens of other
wonderful people, animals and nuts.

VISIT US!

 SIMPLEHAPPYKITCHEN.COM

 SIMPLE_HAPPY_KITCHEN

 SHOP.SIMPLEHAPPYKITCHEN.COM

 @SIMPLEHAPPYKCHN

 SIMPLEHAPPYKITCHEN

IN THIS BOOK

INTRODUCTION

Plant-based lifestyles are more popular than ever, spreading far beyond the vegan and vegetarian communities. This massive movement has made factual and easy-to-understand resources a necessity.

There's just one problem. The resources available are either too complicated or boring – and can even be frightening at times. Those interested in learning the benefits of plant-based nutrition or trying to transition to this diet find it difficult to know how or where to start.

With this in mind, I made it my goal to use my design abilities to promote the values I believe in and help people understand plant-based nutrition in a light-hearted, easy-to-understand way.

Before I started creating this book, I looked at data, charts and articles people were reading and considered how to present them in a better, visual way. I illustrated some food-based characters and published plant-based information on social media featuring these characters. The amazing response and requests for more made me realize this simple approach works and that a full book covering the whole topic could help even more.

My mission in the creation of this book is to expose you to the wonderful, wide variety of plant-based food and the vegan lifestyle, to help you understand what you can do to get all your nutrients in a tasty way and live a better, healthier, compassionate and easier-to-maintain life.

It doesn't matter if you're just curious, if you want to take a step toward this lifestyle, or if you're already there and just want to know more. This book suits everyone, and it's up to you to decide what to do with it.

I was very careful with the information presented in the book and made sure everything was based on research and reliable data. All nutrition information has been verified by professional nutritionists, and every effort was made to make it as accurate as possible.

So, now that we have this introduction out of the way, allow me to introduce you Mr. Pedro Almondovar, a professional almond who will guide you through this joyful journey. Meet him on the next page.

— Miki Mottes

CHAPTER 1:
HI! BUT WHY?

Hello, and welcome to Simple Happy Kitchen!

I'm Pedro Almondovar, a roasted almond. I was elected by majority vote to lead this book, and I intend to do it to the best of my ability. With my help and the help of my friends, you'll learn about the wonderful world of plant-based nutrition, its benefits, and how to adopt it in the most appropriate and easy way.

To make everything simple (and happy), I've divided the book into chapters, and I will accompany you along this wonderful and tasty journey.

In the first chapter, I'll explain the reasons why plant-based nutrition is the best option, debunk myths you may have encountered, and teach you how to make this important change.

JOIN ME!

WHY GO PLANT-BASED?

SUSTAINABILITY

THE RAINFORESTS

WILDLIFE

OUR WATER

COMPASSION

THE ANIMALS

PEACE

OUR PLANET

THE YUMMY FOOD

OUR HEALTH

SHATTERING THE MYTHS

VEGANS ARE DESTROYING THE RAINFORESTS TO MAKE TOFU!

Actually, if anyone's destroying the rainforests, it's the animal farming industry. Most of the land cleared in the Amazon is used as pasture land for animals raised for food – not for growing soybeans. In fact, a vast majority of soybeans grown worldwide are used to feed animals grown for food.

A VEGAN DIET WILL MAKE ME TOO WEAK FOR SPORTS!

Are world-champion power-lifters, NFL stars and MLS players weak? Many successful athletes follow a vegan diet. They've found it doesn't hinder their performance – it helps it.

WE NEED MILK FOR STRONG BONES!

Don't fall victim to milk marketing hype. We do need calcium and vitamin D, but milk doesn't have a monopoly on these nutrients.

A VEGAN DIET IS DANGEROUS FOR CHILDREN!

A vegan diet can be healthy and suitable for people of all ages. As with any diet, one simply has to include the right foods in the right quantities. Many parents out there are raising healthy, happy vegan children!

COWS HAVE TO BE MILKED OR THEY'LL EXPLODE!

Umm...no, they don't. Cows only produce milk if they're pregnant – just like humans. Dairy farmers impregnate cows each year so the milk supply stays steady. If left to their natural cycle, cows make just enough milk for their newborns and don't need to be milked by hand.

ONLY RICH PEOPLE CAN GO VEGAN – IT'S JUST TOO EXPENSIVE!

Actually, it's cheaper to eat a plant-based diet than a meat-centered diet. If your budget is limited, then beans, grains, fruits and vegetables are ideal. These are some of the cheapest and healthiest things you can buy at any supermarket.

IF YOU WERE STRANDED ON A DESERT ISLAND, YOU COULDN'T AVOID EATING ANIMAL FOODS!

Really? What's the likelihood of this happening? It's not useful to think about such hypotheticals when an easy, harm-reducing lifestyle is available here and now. Besides, those small islands are more likely to have a collection of fresh fruits and vegetables than a thriving animal community. So don't sweat it!

VEGAN DIETS AREN'T SAFE FOR PREGNANT WOMEN!

If you're eating healthily for one, you'll be eating healthily for two. According to the American Dietetic Association, a well-planned vegan diet is appropriate for any person, in any stage of life, including when pregnant.

PLANTS FEEL PAIN TOO!

Plants have no central nervous system, nerve endings or brains. They cannot feel pain.

FISH DON'T FEEL PAIN!

Science says otherwise. Unlike plants, fish do have pain receptors. They also produce substances called enkephalins, which mediate pain in the same way they do in vertebrates like us.

WHAT MAKES A WELL-BALANCED PLANT-BASED DIET GOOD FOR YOU?

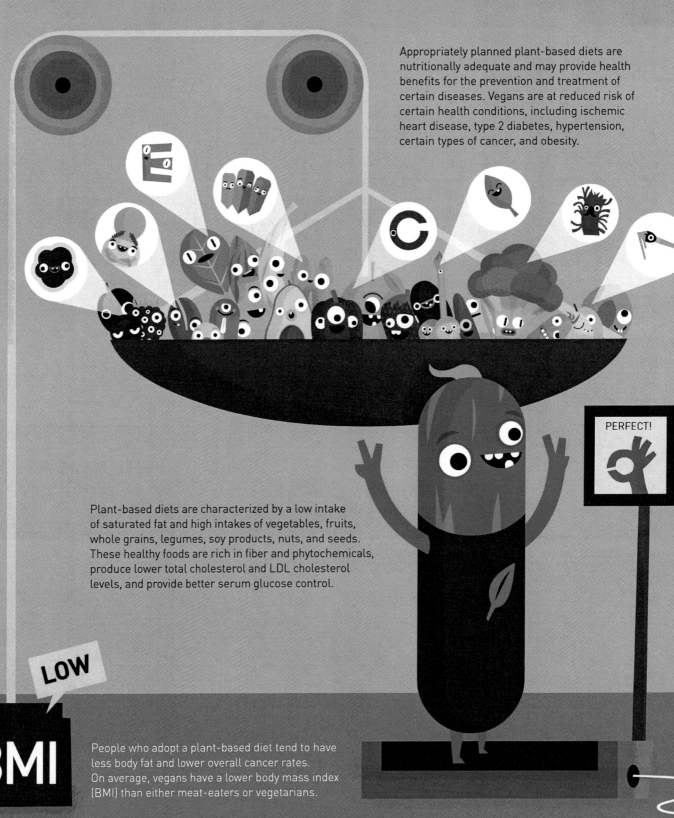

Appropriately planned plant-based diets are nutritionally adequate and may provide health benefits for the prevention and treatment of certain diseases. Vegans are at reduced risk of certain health conditions, including ischemic heart disease, type 2 diabetes, hypertension, certain types of cancer, and obesity.

Plant-based diets are characterized by a low intake of saturated fat and high intakes of vegetables, fruits, whole grains, legumes, soy products, nuts, and seeds. These healthy foods are rich in fiber and phytochemicals, produce lower total cholesterol and LDL cholesterol levels, and provide better serum glucose control.

PERFECT!

LOW

BMI

People who adopt a plant-based diet tend to have less body fat and lower overall cancer rates. On average, vegans have a lower body mass index (BMI) than either meat-eaters or vegetarians.

HOW COULD A NON-PLANT-BASED DIET BE BAD FOR YOU?

EXPERTS SAY:
Many world-wide health organizations recommend reducing meat intake.

SALMONELLA POISONING:
Animal products may be contaminated with Salmonella. Cooking typically destroys this bacteria. However, it is highly contagious, so if it is present, it can contaminate all work spaces and tools in your kitchen or refrigerator.

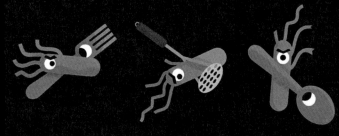

EXCESS IRON INTAKE RISKS:
High intake of iron, especially dietary heme iron, has been recently associated with health risks including type 2 diabetes, coronary heart disease and cardiovascular mortality.

ANTIBIOTICS COMPLICATIONS: According to the CDC, antibiotic resistance reduces our ability to treat infections and poses a serious threat to public health. How does this resistance happen? Animals receive huge amounts of antibiotics, which creates resistant bacteria that can multiply and spread. These bacteria infect food and cause illness. Resistant infections may cause mild to severe illness and can even be fatal. Roughly 20% of resistant infections are caused by germs from the livestock industry.

MERCURY DAMAGE: High levels of mercury in the body can cause serious harm to the nervous system of a fetus or young child. Nearly all fish and shellfish contain traces of this element, and some are packed with it. Eating large amounts of these products can cause dangerously high mercury levels.

STAYING TRIM:
Research has shown that it is easier to maintain weight on a diet that excludes meat, dairy and eggs.

CHAPTER 2

HOW?

Now that you understand the "why" behind a plant-based lifestyle, you're probably asking yourself what you should do with that knowledge.

Don't worry – that's why I'm here!

I'll explain what you can buy, what you should pay attention to while you shop, and the best ways to store what you purchase.

You'll meet many of my friends – legumes, grains, oils, leafy greens, vegetables, fruits, seeds and nuts.

UNDERSTANDING THE
NUTRITION FACTS LABEL

The nutrition facts label is important for anyone who cares about their health, and it's crucial for vegans. It helps us avoid unwanted ingredients, understand what our food is made of and learn what nutrients it contains. A visit to the supermarket without knowing how to read labels can be confusing.

SATURATED FAT: Found in higher proportions in animal products. Exceptions include certain tropical plant oils.

TRANS FAT: Not naturally occurring. Formed by processing vegetable oil to make it more solid and extend shelf-life.

SODIUM: Essential nutrient needed in small amounts. Important for many body processes. High amounts can be harmful.

DIETARY FIBER: Carbohydrate that the human body cannot digest therefore does not provide energy/calories. Found only in plant foods.

PROTEIN: Component of every cell in the human body and essential for all organ functions. Protein foods are important sources of many vitamins and minerals. Every gram of protein provides 4 calories.

CALCIUM: Main component of bones and teeth. Also important in the regulation of neuromuscular activity.

POTASSIUM: Helps maintain normal water and acid-base balance in the body and regulates neuromuscular activity.

SERVING SIZE: Standardized for easier food comparisons. Shown as units (cups, pieces, etc.) followed by the number of grams each serving contains. The serving size affects the calorie and nutrient counts listed on the label.

Nutrition Facts
17 servings per container
Serving size 1 slice (37g)

Amount per serving
Calories 89

	% Daily Value *
Total Fat 1g	2%
Saturated Fat 0g	0%
Trans Fat 0g	
Cholesterol 0mg	0%
Sodium 120mg	5%
Total Carbohydrate 15g	6%
Dietary Fiber 3g	12%
Total Sugars 2g	
Includes 0g Added Sugars	0%
Protein 5g	
Vitamin D 0mcg	0%
Calcium 10mg	1%
Iron 0.7mg	4%
Potassium 70mg	2%

* The % Daily Value (DV) tells you how much a nutrient in a serving of food contributes to a daily diet. 2,000 calories a day is used for general nutrition advice.

Ingredients: Whole Grain Wheat Flour, Wheat Flour, Water, Oat Bran, Oats, Sunflower Seeds, Vinegar, Sea Salt, Yeast.
Contains: Wheat.

INGREDIENTS: The label lists each ingredient by its common name, in descending order by weight. So, the first listed ingredient contributes the most to the product's weight.

CALORIES: The energy our body needs to perform any action, from exercise to sleep. Labels may list calorie counts under the heading of kilocalories or energy.

% DAILY VALUE (DV): The portion of recommended daily intake for each nutrient that the food contains. Based on a 2,000 or 2,500 calorie diet.

CHOLESTEROL: Substance necessary for several body functions. It is produced by the liver, so it isn't necessary to get it from food. Found in animals products.

TOTAL CARBOHYDRATE: Family of compounds including starch, sugars and fiber. Main source of energy for the body and brain. Each ounce provides 4 calories.

TOTAL SUGARS / ADDED SUGARS: Sweet-tasting carbohydrates; includes natural sugars (in fruit) and added sugars (sucrose, syrups, etc.)

VITAMIN D: Responsible for increasing calcium and phosphate absorption in the intestine and promoting bone health.

IRON: Nutrient present in every body cell. Carries oxygen through the body and acts as key component in many processes.

BUILDING A HEALTHY SHOPPING LIST

Changing your shopping list to avoid animal products can be challenging and confusing – but it doesn't have to be! The following guide will help you plan your next visit to the supermarket and make it more efficient, cheaper and healthier.

VEGETABLES

Include as many vegetables as possible in your daily diet. It's best to combine vegetables of all types – fresh, cooked, and frozen. If you buy any processed vegetables (preserved, cooked, etc.), read the ingredients and note the sugar and salt contents. If you frequently use a particular vegetable when cooking, try using it fresh, if possible. For example, beets can be eaten fresh or cooked. Buy various spice vegetables and use them with entrees, soups and salads. These vegetables will help boost the nutritional value of the food. They will also enrich the food in color and flavor, thus reducing the amount of salt needed.
Tip: At least once every two weeks, buy a vegetable that you don't usually buy or have never tried.

FRUITS

Buy fresh and frozen fruit of various colors, from a variety of families: tree fruits, citrus fruits, berries. You can also include dried fruits or fruit juices, but note that dried fruits are sometimes preserved or processed. This means they contain added sugar. Fruit juices are also not as good as fresh fruits, because they lose vitamin content over time and their fiber content is lower.

LEGUMES

Include as many legumes as possible in your diet. Add them to dishes, make them in patties, or include them in soups, sauces and more. Try different types to learn which works best in various recipes. Befriend the tofu! It is available in a variety of textures that can be used for different purposes, from cheese, to steak and even desserts. Some stores stock a variety of products made from legumes, such as flour and noodles. Try them! There are also many meat substitutes based on legumes – especially soy. These can be found in the refrigerated section. Use legume products as a great snack or as an easy meal when you're tired or don't have cooking supplies handy. Remember, these products are processed, so be sure to read the labels and avoid sugar, salt and other unhealthy ingredients as much as possible.

NUTS & SEEDS

Try a variety of nuts and seeds. Combine them for a snack mix or add them to salads or dishes. Each nut or seed has specific advantages, so combining different types will provide a variety of benefits. You can also eat nuts and seeds as spreads. Tahini and peanut butter are the most common, but you can now get almost any nut or seed in this form. When choosing these products, ensure that sugar, salt and fat are not added, and select those that use the whole grain/seed when possible.

GRAINS

A wide range of whole-grain products are available – breads, pastas, noodles, crackers, and more. Try them! Some will surprise you with their taste and texture. Do you like products that contain whole flour? Great! Choose these over similar products with non-whole grain. Try new grains that you haven't experienced: quinoa in different colors, teff, millet, bulgur, buckwheat of various kinds. Try using the grains you already know in different ways, such as in porridge, salads or new dishes. When baking, substitute half of the non-whole-wheat flour in the recipe with rye, teff or whole-wheat flour.

NUTRITION FACTS LABEL:
WHAT TO LOOK FOR & WHAT TO AVOID

Nutrition Facts	
4 servings per container	
Serving size 1 cup (240ml)	

Amount per serving	
Calories	**70**

	% Daily Value *
Total Fat 5g	**7%**
Saturated Fat 1g	3%
Trans Fat 0g	
Cholesterol 0mg	**0%**
Sodium 105mg	**4%**
Total Carbohydrate 7g	**2%**
Dietary Fiber 1g	2%
Total Sugars 6g	
Includes 5.5g Added Sugars	10%
Protein 1g	
Vitamin D 2mcg	10%
Calcium 300mg	23%
Iron 0mg	0%
Potassium 24mg	1%

* The % Daily Value (DV) tells you how much a nutrient in a serving of food contributes to a daily diet. 2,000 calories a day is used for general nutrition advice.

Ingredients: Macadamia Milk (Filtered Water, Macadamias), Cane Sugar, Calcium Phosphate, Natural Flavors, Locust Bean Gum, Sea Salt, Sunflower Lecitin, Gellan Gum, Vitamin A Palmitate, Vitamin D2, Vitamin B12.
Contains: Macadamias

The %DV makes it easy for you to compare foods. You can compare the calories and nutrient content of two products to decide which you prefer. Just make sure the serving sizes are similar.

Don't understand the name of one of the ingredients? Google it. Maybe it's not that bad. Don't understand the names of several ingredients? Consider choosing a different product.

Cholesterol is a compound found in animal products only. If a product's label includes a cholesterol amount other than zero, you know it's not vegan.

Look for nutrient-dense foods that contain a high percentage of vitamins and minerals but are not high in calories, sugar and fat.

Look for products that provide adequate amounts of calcium, fiber, iron, potassium and vitamin D.

Limit your use of products that contain large amounts of sugars, salt or fat - especially saturated and trans fat.

THE SIMPLE HAPPY GUIDE TO SPICES

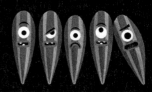

ROSEMARY
Light green in color with a strong fragrance and pine-needle shape. Hardy plant that endures cold weather.

CORIANDER
Hails from Argentina and Morocco. Cilantro seed that offers a light fragrance.

OREGANO
Indigenous to Mexico and Italy. Provides a strong taste, similar to marjoram, but more powerful.

CUMIN
Similar in appearance to caraway but a shade lighter. Native to Syria and Mexico.

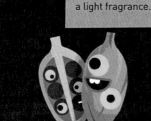
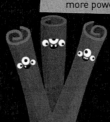

CHILI POWDER
Ranges from mild to hot. Combination of chili pepper, oregano, ground cumin and allspice.

CARDAMOM
Small, sweet and fragrant seeds. Grown in Guatemala and India.

CINNAMON
Grown in East India. The strong-scented bark of the cassia or cinnamon tree.

CAYENNE PEPPER
Potent, spicy red pepper. Hails from French Guiana.

CLOVES
Dried clover-tree blossom offering a strong, sweet taste. Grown in Indonesia.

GINGER
Lumpy, brown tropical-plant root.

THYME
Small leaf, brownish-green in color, with strong fragrance.

PAPRIKA
Made from dried red peppers.

NUTMEG
Native to the Netherlands, East and West Indies. Seed of the nutmeg, offers sweet taste and fragrance.

BAY LEAVES
Similar to sassafras with strong aroma, oblong shape and dark-green coloring.

TURMERIC ROOT
Bright-yellow root with mild pepper flavor. Part of the ginger family.

BASIL
Green leaf with pleasant fragrance. Part of the mint family.

GARLIC POWDER
Garlic cloves, dried and ground.

STAR ANISE
Grown in Spain, Syria and China. Tastes like licorice.

THE E-NUMBERS DICTIONARY

E-Numbers are codes for substances that are permitted to be used as food additives.

Ethical consumers want to know what is in the food they eat. When reading ingredient lists, it is often easy to spot the animal-derived ingredients, but not always. Use this complete listing which details whether the E-Numbers are of animal origin or cruelty-free. There are many apps available to help you check E-numbers while you shop. Try them!

NEVER VEGAN

Avoid these E-Numbers, as they are always of animal origin.

E120	Carmine Dye from Cochineal Beetles	E910	L-cysteine
E441	Gelatine	E913	Lanolin, Sheep wool grease
E542	Edible Bone Phosphate	E920	L-cysteine
E901	Beeswax, white and yellow	E921	L-cysteine
E904	Shellac, Resin from Lac bug	E966	Lactitol

POSSIBLY NOT VEGAN

These E-Numbers could be of vegan or animal origin. Check with the supplier periodically to determine which source they use for each product.

E153	Carbon black, Vegetable carbon
E161g	Canthaxanthin
E161h	Zeaxanthin
E161i	Citranaxanthin
E161j	Astaxanthin
E252	Potassium nitrate (Saltpetre)
E270	Lactic acid
E322	Lecithin
E325	Sodium lactate
E326	Potassium lactate
E327	Calcium lactate
E422	Glycerol
E430	Polyoxyethylene (8) stearate
E431	Polyoxyethylene (40) stearate
E432	Polyoxyethylene (20) sorbitan monolaurate (polysorbate 20)
E433	Polyoxyethylene (20) sorbitan monooleate (polysorbate 80)
E434	Polyoxyethylene (20) sorbitan monopalmitate (polysorbate 40)
E435	Polyoxyethylene (20) sorbitan monostearate (polysorbate 60)
E436	Polyoxyethylene (20) sorbitan tristearate (polysorbate 65)
E442	Ammonium phosphatides
E470A	Sodium, potassium and calcium salts of fatty acids
E470B	Magnesium salts of fatty acids
E471	Mono- and diglycerides of fatty acids
E472A	Acetic acid esters of mono- and diglycerides of fatty acids

E472B	Lactic acid esters of mono- and diglycerides of fatty acid
E472C	Citric acid esters of mono- and diglycerides of fatty acids
E472D	Tartaric acid esters of mono- and diglycerides of fatty acids
E472E	Mono- and diacetyl tartaric acid esters of mono- and diglycerides of fatty acids
E472F	Mixed acetic and tartaric acid esters of mono- and diglycerides of fatty acids
E473	Sucrose esters of fatty acids
E474	Sucroglycerides
E475	Polyglycerol esters of fatty acids
E476	Polyglycerol polyricinoleate
E477	Propane-1, 2-diol esters of fatty acids, propylene glycol esters of fatty acids
E478	Lactylated fatty acid esters of glycerol and propane-1
E479b	Thermally oxidized soya bean oil interacted with mono and diglycerides of fatty acids

E481	Sodium stearoyl-2-lactylate
E482	Calcium stearoyl-2-lactylate
E483	Stearyl tartrate
E491	Sorbitan monostearate
E492	Sorbitan tristearate
E493	Sorbitan monolaurate
E494	Sorbitan monooleate
E495	Sorbitan monopalmitate
E570	Stearic acid
E572	Magnesium stearate, calcium stearate
E585	Ferrous lactate
E627	Disodium guanylate, sodium guanylate
E631	Disodium inosinate
E635	Disodium 5′-ribonucleotides
E640	Glycine and its sodium salt

ALWAYS VEGAN

These E-Numbers are definitely vegan! They are derived solely from mineral or vegetable sources. Just remember – vegan doesn't automatically mean healthy!

FOOD COLORINGS

E100 E101 E101a E102 E103 E104 E105 E106 E107 E110 E111 E121
E122 E123 E124 E125 E126 E127 E128 E129 E130 E131 E132 E133
E140 E141 E142 E143 E150a E150b E150c E150d E151 E152 E154 E155
E160a E160b E160c E160d E160e E160f E161a E161b E161c E161d
E161e E161f E162 E163 E170 E171 E172 E173 E174 E175 E180 E181

PRESERVATIVES

E200 E201 E202 E203 E210 E211 E212 E213 E214 E215 E216 E217
E218 E219 E220 E221 E222 E223 E224 E225 E226 E227 E228 E230
E231 E232 E233 E234 E235 E236 E237 E238 E239 E240 E242 E249
E250 E251 E260 E261 E262 E263 E264 E280 E281 E282 E283 E284
E285 E290 E296 E297

ANTIOXIDANTS

E300 E301 E302 E303 E304 E306 E307 E308 E309 E310 E311 E312
E315 E316 E317 E318 E319 E320 E321 E329 E330 E331 E332 E333
E334 E335 E336 E337 E338 E339 E340 E341 E343 E350 E351 E352
E353 E354 E355 E356 E357 E363 E365 E366 E367 E370 E375 E380
E381 E385 E400 E401 E402 E403 E404 E405 E406 E407 E407a E410
E412 E413 E414 E415 E416 E417 E418 E420 E421 E425 E440 E444
E445 E450 E451 E452 E459 E460 E461 E462 E463 E464 E465 E466
E468 E469

FLAVOR ENHANCERS

E620 E621 E622 E623 E624 E625 E626 E628 E629 E630 E632 E633
E634 E636 E637

ANTI-CAKING AGENTS

E500 E501 E503 E504 E507 E508 E509 E510 E511 E512 E513 E517
E518 E519 E520 E521 E522 E523 E524 E525 E526 E527 E528 E529
E530 E535 E536 E538 E540 E541 E543 E544 E545 E550 E551 E552
E553b E554 E555 E556 E558 E559 E574 E575 E576 E577 E578 E579

MISCELLANEOUS

E900 E902 E903 E905 E905a E905b E905c E906 E907 E908 E912 E914
E915 E922 E923 E924 E925 E926 E927 E297b E928 E930 E938 E939
E940 E941 E942 E943a E943b E944 E948 E949 E950 E951 E952 E953
E954 E955 E957 E959 E965 E967 E999

ADDITIONAL CHEMICALS

E1103 E1105 E1106 E1107 E1108 E1109 E1110 E1111 E1112 E1113
E1114 E1115 E1116 E1117 E1118 E1119 E1120 E1121 E1122 E1123
E1124 E1125 E1126 E1127 E1128 E1129 E1130 E1131 E1132 E1133
E1134 E1135 E1136 E1137 E1138 E1139 E1140 E1141 E1142 E1143
E1144 E1145 E1146 E1147 E1148 E1149 E1150 E1151 E1152 E1153
E1154 E1155 E1156 E1157 E1158 E1159 E1160 E1161 E1162 E1163
E1164 E1165 E1166 E1167 E1168 E1169 E1170 E1171 E1172 E1173
E1174 E1175 E1176 E1177 E1178 E1179 E1180 E1181 E1182 E1183
E1184 E1185 E1186 E1187 E1188 E1189 E1190 E1191 E1192 E1193
E1194 E1195 E1196 E1197 E1198 E1199 E1200 E1201 E1202 E1400
E1401 E1402 E1403 E1404 E1410 E1412 E1413 E1414 E1420 E1421
E1422 E1430 E1440 E1441 E1442 E1450 E1451 E1505 E1510 E1518
E1520

GROCERY STORAGE GUIDE

1 BELL PEPPER
Refrigerator shelf
Plastic bag
1 week

2 CITRUS
Refrigerator shelf
Unwrapped
2 weeks

3 CITRUS (HALVED)
Refrigerator shelf
Plastic-wrapped
2-3 days

4 GINGER (CUT)
Refrigerator shelf
Plastic bag + paper
towel
1-2 weeks

5 BEET
Refrigerator shelf
Plastic bag
2 weeks

6 ASPARAGUS
Refrigerator shelf
Stems in water,
lightly covered
with plastic
2 weeks

7 MELON (HALVED)
Refrigerator shelf
Plastic-wrapped
7-10 days

8 SALAD GREENS
Refrigerator drawer
Plastic container
layered with
paper towels
10 days

9 GREEN BEANS
Refrigerator drawer
Plastic bag + paper
towel
1 week

10 CARROTS
Refrigerator drawer
Plastic bag
3 weeks

11 APPLE
Refrigerator drawer
Unwrapped
3 weeks

12 AVOCADO (HALVED)
Refrigerator shelf
Brushed with
lemon juice,
plastic-wrapped
1 day

13 BROCCOLI
Refrigerator drawer
Plastic bag
3 weeks

14 GRAPES
Refrigerator drawer
Perforated plastic
bag
1-2 weeks

15 BERRIES
Refrigerator drawer
Uncovered, vented
container
3-5 days

16 HEAD OF LETTUCE
Refrigerator drawer
Plastic bag + paper
towel
5 days

17 CUCUMBER
Refrigerator drawer
Plastic-wrapped
1 week

18 CAULIFLOWER
Refrigerator drawer
Plastic-wrapped
5 days

19 CABBAGE
Refrigerator drawer
plastic-wrapped
2 weeks

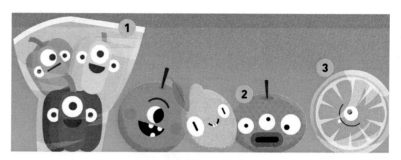
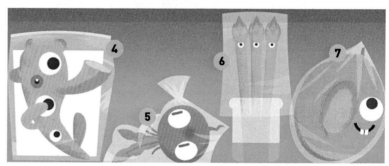
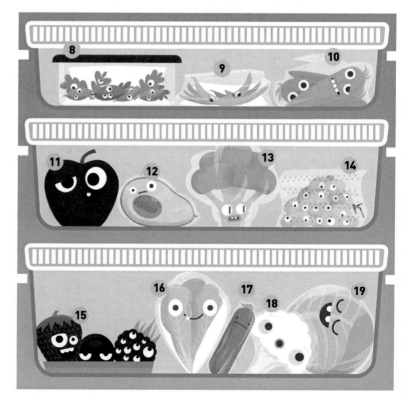

20 GINGER
Refrigerator shelf
Unwrapped
1 month

21 MUSHROOM
Refrigerator shelf
Paper bag
3 days

22 RADISH
Refrigerator shelf
Plastic bag + paper towel
2 weeks

23 BANANA
Countertop
Unwrapped
3 days once ripe

24 PEAR
Countertop
Unwrapped
4 days once ripe

25 TOMATO
Countertop
Unwrapped,
vented container
5 days

26 MELON
Countertop
Unwrapped
5 days once ripe

27 PEACH
Countertop to ripen,
Refrigerator shelf when ripe
Unwrapped
5 days once ripe

28 AVOCADO
Countertop to ripen,
Refrigerator shelf when ripe
Unwrapped
4 days once ripe

29 PLUM
Countertop to ripen,
Refrigerator shelf when ripe
Unwrapped
5 days once ripe

30 SWEET POTATO
Dark pantry
Paper bag
2 weeks

31 ONION
Dark pantry
Unwrapped
1-2 months

32 GARLIC
Dark pantry
Unwrapped
2 months

33 POTATO
Dark pantry
Unwrapped
1-2 months

34 WINTER SQUASH
Dark pantry
Unwrapped
2 months

35 GINGER CAT
The cat is not a food.
Don't eat the cat.

FOOD STORAGE HACKS

USE THESE METHODS TO MAKE YOUR FOODS HAPPIER WHILE IN STORAGE.

BRUSH AVOCADO HALVES WITH LEMON JUICE OR OLIVE OIL.

To preserve cut avocados, brush the open ends with lemon juice or olive oil. This protects the fruit from oxidation, so it doesn't turn brown.

NEED TO QUICKLY RIPEN AN AVOCADO? USE A BANANA!
Ripe bananas release the hormone ethylene, which triggers ripening in mature fruit. Place the banana in a closed paper bag with under-ripe avocados to speed up the process.

STORE MILK IN GLASS BOTTLES.

These do a better job of sealing than cardboard cartons. Glass bottles also get colder, so your milk stays fresh longer.

WRAP THE CROWN OF A BANANA BUNCH WITH PLASTIC WRAP.
It will make them last 3-5 days longer than usual.

DON'T WASH YOUR PRODUCE BEFORE YOU PUT IT IN THE FRIDGE.

The dampness can encourage mold and rot.

DON'T PUT BREAD IN THE FRIDGE.

Cold temperatures (but not freezing) cause the starch in bread to regroup more quickly than it would in a warmer environment, which makes it stale.

TO PREVENT PEANUT BUTTER FROM SEPARATING, STORE IT UPSIDE DOWN.

The oil will seep back into the peanut butter and work its way to the bottom of the jar.

CUT THE GREEN TOPS OFF YOUR CARROTS TO LOCK IN NUTRIENTS.

The leaves of root veggies steal their nutrients - even after they've been picked!

THE OILY BIBLE

Oil is the extract from the fatty part of a seed, nut, fruit or grain, therefore it lacks important substances such as fiber, proteins, vitamins and minerals. It is always better to use the oil's food source rather than the oil itself. The advantage of vegetable oils over animal fat is that they do not contain cholesterol and often contain lower amounts of saturated fat – two things health organizations recommend we reduce in our diet. Many vegetable oils are also good sources of vitamin E & K and sterols that contribute to good health.

OLIVE

Attributed with many health benefits. Staple in the healthy Mediterranean diet. Rich in omega-9, Vitamins E & K.

🌡 419 °F / 215 °C (Virgin)

CANOLA

Good source of omega-3 and vitamins E & K.

🌡 399 °F / 204 °C

SUNFLOWER

Good source of vitamin E.

🌡 475 °F / 246 °C (Linoleic)

CORN

Source of vitamin E.

🌡 457 °F / 236 °C

COCONUT

Very high in saturated fat. Good as a butter substitute and for cosmetic uses.

🌡 351 °F / 177 °C (Extra virgin)

ALMOND

Good source of vitamin E.

🌡 430 °F / 221 °C

SOY

Good source of omega-6 and omega-3. Rich in vitamin K. Source of vitamin E.

🌡 466 °F / 241 °C

HEMP

Good source of omega-3.

🌡 329 °F / 165 °C

SESAME

Unique taste – great for Asian dishes.

🌡 410 °F / 210 °C

AVOCADO

Rich in omega-9 fatty acids.

🌡 520 °F / 271 °C

RICE BRAN

Source of vitamin E.

🌡 489 °F / 254 °C

FLAXSEED

Richest source of omega-3. Source of vitamin E.

🌡 225 °F / 107 °C

The smoke point is the temperature at which oil starts to break down and lose its flavor and nutritional value. Oils are heat sensitive, so it's important to choose the right one for each task. For short frying and seasoning, use olive oil. For deep frying, use canola or soy oil. For any other use that does not require heating (salads, spreads, etc.), use your favorite based on flavor. It's best to minimize frying as much as possible. If you choose to fry, use very little oil.

LEAFY-GREEN GUIDE

Green leaves are among the richest sources of nutrition in nature, packing lots of nutritional value in just a few calories. These green powerhouses provide minimal fat and calories but deliver large doses of vitamins, minerals and antioxidants. They are great sources of calcium, vitamin K, folic acid, magnesium and beta-carotene.

ARUGULA
Source of vitamin K

KALE
Source of iron, rich in vitamin C, lutein & zeaxanthin

ROMAINE LETTUCE
Rich in vitamin C, lutein & zeaxanthin

SWISS CHARD
Rich in vitamin C, lutein & zeaxanthin

WATERCRESS
Rich in vitamin C, lutein & zeaxanthin

SPINACH
Rich in vitamin C, lutein & zeaxanthin

COLLARD GREENS
Rich in vitamin C, lutein & zeaxanthin

BOK CHOY
Rich in vitamin C

BEET GREENS
Rich in vitamin C and iron

ENDIVE
Source of vitamin K

SPEARMINT
High in vitamin A and iron

ICEBERG LETTUCE

BASIL
High in vitamins A and K

MUSTARD GREENS
Rich in vitamin C, lutein & zeaxanthin

PARSLEY
High in vitamins A, C, K, iron and calcium

TURNIP GREENS
Rich in vitamin C, lutein & zeaxanthin

CABBAGE
Rich in vitamin C

COMMON LEGUMES

Legumes are a family of plants that grow their seeds in pods. Humans have looked to legumes for their protein for more than 5,000 years. These plants are also a rich source of fiber, micronutrients and phytochemicals. Meet some legendary legumes!

CHICKPEA: A favorite for falafel and hummus. Archaeologists have found evidence of chickpea cultivation in the Middle East as far back as 7,500 years. This makes the chickpea one of the earliest cultivated legumes.

GREEN LENTIL: The lentil family is colorful and tasty. The green variety is the most famous. We get the word "lens" from the word "lentil." Lenses were named after the legume because double-convex lenses look just like lentils!

SOYBEAN: This is the queen of legumes. It contains the best quality of protein among legumes, making it a widely-used substitute for meat and dairy.

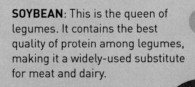

BLACK EYED PEA: Also called a cowpea, black eyed *peas* are actually a bean!

WHITE BEAN: This bean's claim to fame hails from ancient Greece. Minor Grecian public officials were elected by placing one white bean inside a "bean machine" with an entire load of black beans. Whoever picked the white bean got the job.

LUPINI BEANS: These make such great snacks, beer bars serve them as appetizers. Simply soak them in salty water to pickle them. These beans also provide a striking plant in a brilliant array of colors.

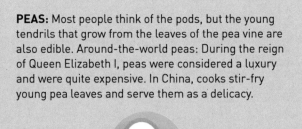

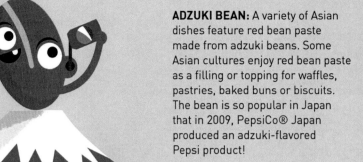

PEAS: Most people think of the pods, but the young tendrils that grow from the leaves of the pea vine are also edible. Around-the-world peas: During the reign of Queen Elizabeth I, peas were considered a luxury and were quite expensive. In China, cooks stir-fry young pea leaves and serve them as a delicacy.

ADZUKI BEAN: A variety of Asian dishes feature red bean paste made from adzuki beans. Some Asian cultures enjoy red bean paste as a filling or topping for waffles, pastries, baked buns or biscuits. The bean is so popular in Japan that in 2009, PepsiCo® Japan produced an adzuki-flavored Pepsi product!

We're **NOT** nuts!

NUTS

PEANUT: Don't let the name confuse you. The peanut is not a nut, but a legume related to lentils and beans. It's so popular, March has been named National Peanut Month and November is National Peanut Butter Lovers Month. These legumes are galactic travelers! Astronaut Alan B. Shepard brought a peanut with him to the moon.

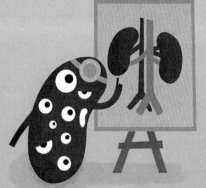

RED BEAN: Due to its resemblance in shape and color to the kidney, red beans are also called kidney beans. Red kidney beans should not be confused with other red beans, such as adzuki beans.

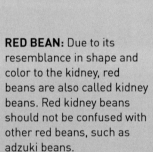

FAVA BEAN: Fava beans have been popular for a long time – although not with everyone. A hereditary condition, G6PD (Favism) causes an allergic-like reaction to fava beans.

MUNG BEAN: This bean allows for spontaneity. It can be cooked without soaking or even eaten without cooking (after soaking). It sprouts quickly and then looks like a unicorn!

BLACK BEAN: Born in Central America. Can be used for spreads and tortilla filling. It likes hot salsas!

HUMMUS

ONION

PITA BREAD

CHICKPEAS

PARSLEY

TAHINI

CUMIN & PAPRIKA

OLIVE OIL

OLIVES & PICKLES

HUMMUS RECIPE (SERVES 3)

1 Add 1 tbsp baking soda to 250g dried chickpeas and soak in refrigerator overnight. **2** Drain and rinse. **3** Place the chickpeas and 5 peeled garlic cloves in water and bring to a boil, then simmer for about one hour – until the chickpeas are tender. **4** Drain, setting aside ½ cup of the water and ¼ of chickpeas. **5** Let the chickpeas cool a bit. Puree the chickpeas, ½ cup of the reserved water, and 5 garlic cloves in a food processor. Add a dash of salt, ¼ cup tahini, ¼ tbsp ground cumin, and the juice from 2 lemons. Process until you achieve a creamy texture, then transfer to a serving bowl. **6** Clean the food processor, then puree 2 tbsp lemon juice, ¼ cup tahini, and 1 peeled garlic clove. **7** Create an indentation in the center of the hummus (a spoon works great for this). Fill this with the sauce and some olive oil. Top the hummus with a sprinkle of paprika and cumin. **8** Use the reserved whole chickpeas and some parsley as garnish. Serve with your favorites – pickled cucumbers, olives, onion or pita bread.

Nutrition values for 1 serving (about 1 cup)
Calories: 435 • Protein: 20g • Calcium: 133mg • Zinc: 3mg • Dietary fiber: 12g

With few ingredients, hummus is simple to make. Its staples are chickpeas, tahini, lemon, and garlic. To create variety, use different serving methods or create different consistencies. Go heavy on the chickpeas or on the tahini. Crown your hummus with pine nuts or grilled mushrooms, or garnish with fava beans. Make it your own!

THE LEGUMES
SOAKING, COOKING & SIZE GUIDE

SOAKING TIME

COOKING TIME

SIZE AFTER COOKING

CHICKPEAS

8 h 2-3 h x2

ANASAZI BEANS

6 h 1 h x2

BLACK BEANS

4 h 1-1½ h x2

SOYBEANS
10 h 2 h x3

BROWN LENTILS

8 h 50 min x2

FAVA BEANS

10 h 50 min x2

ADZUKI BEANS

4 h 1 h x3

BLACK EYED PEAS

1½ h 1 h x2

GREEN PEAS

10 h 2 h x2

GREEN SPLIT PEAS

10 h 45 min x2

YELLOW SPLIT PEAS

10 h 1½ h x2

MUNG BEANS

10 h 1 h x2

CANNELLINI BEANS

10 h 1 h x2

GREEN LENTILS

8 h 45 min x2

RED LENTILS

2 h 25 min x2

YELLOW LENTILS

8 h 25 min x2

LIMA BEANS

10 h 1 h x2½

KIDNEY BEANS

7 h 1 h x2

NAVY BEANS

7 h 1 h x2½

PINTO BEANS
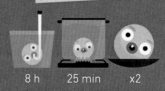
8 h 1½ h x2

THE INCREDIBLE BENEFITS OF
SOAKING & SPROUTING

Soaking and sprouting is a simple, time-tested practice that offers huge nutritional benefits. You can do this with almost any unsliced grains, seeds, legumes or nuts.

This process removes a lot of the phytic acid and other inhibitors. This makes protein and minerals (like iron, calcium and zinc) that were locked up inside the seed, bean or grain, more available for us to absorb. It also increases some vitamin content. Additionally, sprouting makes food easier to digest and therefore can help with issues such as bloating and gas. The easiest foods to sprout are small beans like lentils and mung, as well as wheat and sunflower seeds.

SOAKING & SPROUTING GUIDE

SOAK

Place your seed/grain/legumes in a large mason jar with enough water to submerge them, with an inch or two of water on top. The exact amount of water doesn't matter – it's only for soaking purposes.

WAIT

Soaking and sprouting times vary among different grains, seeds, nuts and legumes. Let it soak for the time period shown for its type:

10 h Adzuki Beans

8 h Alfalfa

24 h Almonds

8 h Amaranth

10 h Black Beans

6 h Buckwheat

10 h Chickpeas

7 h Lentils

5 h Millet

12 h Mung Beans

10 h Navy Beans

6 h Oat Groats

3 h Pumpkin Seeds

4 h Quinoa

8 h Sesame Seeds

8 h Sunflower Seeds

12 h Brown Rice

RINSE

When soaking is complete, rinse thoroughly. Continue rinsing until the water runs clear.

SPROUT & GROW

Rinse with filtered water at least twice a day. The goal is to rinse and drain thoroughly. As it starts to sprout, you'll notice a tiny "tail" start to protrude from the seed. This means it's growing and sprouting! You'll know sprouting is complete when the seeds have a tail, or they've sprouted greens! Let it sprout for the time period shown for its type:

STORE

Keep sprouts fresh by wrapping them in a mesh cheesecloth or nut milk bag and storing them in the fridge. Use within 3-4 days.

2-5 days Alfalfa

3-4 days Adzuki Beans

1-3 days Amaranth

2-3 days Almonds

2-3 days Buckwheat

3-4 days Black Beans

2-3 days Lentils

3-4 days Chickpeas

2-3 days Millet

1-2 days Mung Beans

3 days Navy Beans

2-3 days Oat Groats

Do not sprout Pumpkin Seeds

2-3 days Quinoa

2-3 days Sesame Seeds

1-2 days Sunflower Seeds

3 days Brown Rice

IS SOY GOOD FOR YOU? (YES!)

Found mainly in soy, isoflavones are substances classified as phytoestrogens. This name, however, is misleading, because isoflavones are not the same as the hormone estrogen.

Isoflavones in food may provide some health benefits and are safe for men and women of all ages.

Among legumes, soy has the richest protein composition. It also contains a relatively high amount of fat – mainly essential omega-6 and omega-3. Soy further provides high iron and calcium content. Eating this isoflavone-packed legume has been linked to reduced breast cancer risk, and it may also help lower cholesterol.

According to the World Health Organization, GMOs (genetically modified organisms) currently available on the international market have passed safety assessments and are not likely to pose risks to human health. Additionally, no effects on human health have been linked to the consumption of such foods. If you're still unsure about GMOs, you can avoid them if you prefer. Simply look for "GMO-free" food labels.

Due to these benefits, it is highly recommended to include unprocessed or traditionally processed soy foods such as tofu, tempeh, soy milk, soybeans and edamame in your diet. Research has shown that you can safely eat as much as three servings of soy foods per day as part of a varied diet.

MEET TOFU

WHERE DOES TOFU COME FROM?
Also known as bean curd, tofu is created by coagulating soy milk and pressing the resulting curds into soft white blocks.

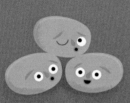 

SOY BEANS → **SOY MILK** → **PRESSED** → **TOFU!**

Tofu is perfect for both savory and sweet dishes due to its subtle flavor. Season or marinate it to complement your dish of choice.

Tofu is available in several varieties. Pressing it longer releases more liquid, creating a more firm tofu.

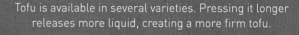

EXTRA FIRM   **FIRM**   **MEDIUM**   **SOFT**   **SILKEN**

All tofus must be rinsed, covered with water and kept in a refrigerated container. To keep tofu fresh for up to one week, change the water often. If you keep it in the original package, you can freeze tofu for up to 5 months. Keep in mind, freezing changes its texture.

Tofu absorbs the flavor of its fellow ingredients.

A great source of calcium!

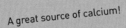

An excellent source of iron!

A good source of protein!

It contains all essential amino acids.

GRAIN COOKING GUIDE

Yield amounts are based on 1 uncooked cup of each grain. Cooking time shown is after bringing to a boil (except oats).

Water cups

AMARANTH: It provides a mild peppery taste and is popular in cereals, breads, muffins, crackers, and pancakes. Makes 2½ cups.

BARLEY: Hulled barley and pearled barley are the most common types. Hulled is more nutritious, but it's chewier. Makes 3½ cups.

FREEKEH: This young, green wheat has been toasted and cracked. It offers a unique flavor. Makes 3 cups.

BUCKWHEAT: It has a unique color and flavor that are often an acquired taste. Makes 2½ cups.

BULGUR: Because this form of wheat is already cracked and boiled, it can be prepared as quickly as dried pasta. Makes 3 cups.

RYE BERRIES: Because this grain is harder to refine than wheat, it retains more of its nutrients. Makes 3 cups.

SPELT: A great substitute for white wheat flour in baked goods. Its husk protects itself from pollutants and insects. Makes 3 cups.

KAMUT®: This grain was once grown by ancient Egyptians and Chinese societies. It is unique among grains because it has not been modified in any way. Makes 3 cups.

MILLET: Its minute size and soft texture make it perfect for a salad or side dish. Makes 4 cups.

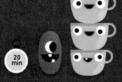

TEFF: This small, gluten-free grain offers a long list of health benefits. It's a species of lovegrass native to Ethiopia, where it's used to make injera and keyta. Makes 3½ cups.

QUINOA: All colors taste basically the same, making varieties interchangeable. They offer a mild and nutty flavor. Makes 3 cups.

SHORT GRAIN RICE: It has a high percentage of starch that makes it sticky. This makes the grains clump together when cooked. Makes 2 cups.

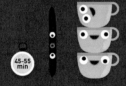

WILD RICE: This is not actually a type of rice but an aquatic grass that bears edible seeds. It grows in wild marshy areas of fresh-water lakes and rivers. Makes 3½ cups.

WHITE BASMATI RICE: This is an aromatic rice that features a nutlike fragrance while cooking and a delicate flavor when eaten. Makes 2 cups.

JASMIN WHITE RICE: This long-grain, aromatic rice is much like basmati, but more affordable. The grains tend to clump together more than those of basmati do. Makes 1½ cups.

BROWN RICE: Only its husk is removed during milling, so this grain is naturally high in vitamins, minerals and dietary fiber. Makes 3 cups.

FARRO: This ancient wheat variety is also known as emmer. It's a staple in Italy. It offers an al dente texture regardless of cooking time, making it a top choice for baked dishes. Makes 2 cups.

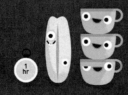

WHEAT BERRIES: These are the parts of wheat kernels that are entirely edible. They have no hull or outer shell, and they include the germ, bran and endosperm. Makes 2½ cups.

ROLLED OATS: These are frequently used in granola bars and baked goods. To process, the grains are steamed then pressed. Heat on low for 5 minutes. Remove from heat, cover, and let stand for 5 minutes before serving. Makes 1-2 cups.

QUICK COOKING OATS: Also known as "instant oats," these are pre-cooked, dried and rolled. Perfect for a creamy oatmeal! Place oats in boiling water and let stand for 3-4 minutes. Makes 1 cup.

CHAPTER 3

SUBSTITUTES

When you switch to plant-based nutrition, you don't have to give up anything you love. I don't like using the word "substitutes" or "replacements," because plant-based food is wonderful in itself and does not need to "replace" anything.

So, if you really want to continue eating the food you already know – but in an ethical and healthy way – I've prepared the next chapter just for you.

I'm wonderful as cheese, btw.

EGG REPLACEMENTS

3 tbsp water
+ 1 tbsp soy flour

⅓ cup water
+ 1 tbsp chia seeds

3 tbsp water
+ 1 tbsp ground flax

¼ cup unsweetened
apple sauce

3 tbsp peanut butter
+ 2 tbsp water

½ mashed
ripe banana

1 tbsp water
+ 2 tbsp corn starch

3 tbsp tahini
+ 2 tbsp water

¼ cup
silk tofu

1 tbsp water
+ 1 tbsp agar agar

Each option replaces **1** egg for baking and cooking

MEAT SUBSTITUTES

The term "meat substitutes" is a bit misleading. These are not recent concoctions created to substitute for meat. Most of the foods discussed here are actually traditional foods that were developed long ago. The main reason they are considered meat alternatives is their protein content and texture. When you purchase a vegan meat alternative, choose natural products over processed. Highly processed foods have higher amounts of salt, fat and sugar. As you shop, remember to read labels and check ingredient lists to find the best options.

TOFU

Tofu is an ancient staple in East Asian and Southeast Asian cuisines. This food is created by coagulating soy milk, then pressing the resulting curds into soft, white blocks. Tofu can be soft, firm or extra firm. It offers a subtle flavor, making it versatile for many dishes. Tofu contains large amounts of protein and iron. Depending on the ingredients used in manufacturing it, tofu can also have a high calcium content.

OKARA

Okara is actually a useful by-product from the creation of other soy foods. It is the pulp that remains after pureed soybeans are filtered during the production of soy milk and tofu. It is typically white or yellowish in color. It has less protein and fat, but much more fiber, than tofu or tempeh. Okara also contains potassium and calcium, and most of the soybean isoflavones are left in it. With so many benefits, it's no surprise this product is part of the traditional cuisines of Japan, Korea and China.

Don't confuse okara with okra, which is the plant grown for its edible pods. It has nothing to do with me!

TEMPEH

Tempeh is a traditional soy product that originates in Indonesia. It has a firm texture and an earthy flavor. Tempeh is made by using a natural culturing and controlled fermentation process that binds soybeans. Unlike tofu, tempeh is made from the whole soybean. Therefore, it has different characteristics and texture. It offers a higher protein content and more dietary fiber and vitamins.

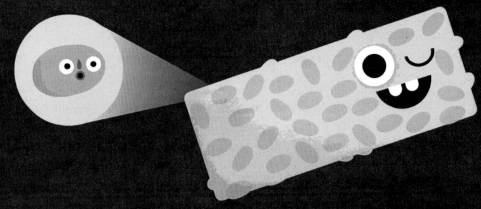

SOYA CHUNKS

Also known as textured or texturized vegetable protein (TVP), textured soy protein (TSP), or soy meat. It is the newest meat substitute, but it's been around for about 50 years. Soya chunks are a defatted soy flour product – a by-product of extracting soybean oil. This means it has minimal oil content but is very high in protein, fiber and minerals. Compared to other soy products, soya chunks are considered more processed.

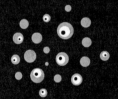

SEITAN

Seitan is believed to have originated more than a thousand years ago in China, as a meat substitute for Buddhists. Its preparation process is simple. It involves washing wheat flour dough with water until all the starch granules have been removed, leaving the gluten (wheat protein). This process makes seitan a low-fat, medium-carbohydrate and high-protein source. Depending on the ingredients used in manufacturing it, seitan can also have a high calcium content.

PLANT-BASED MILK

Plant-based milk makes some of the tastiest things in the world possible: cappuccino, cereal, vegan ice cream and more.

People are becoming aware that cow's milk is not that healthy. They are also learning that the image of happy cows strolling on a grassy knoll is a far cry from the real suffering cows endure on dairy farms.

Fortunately, there are several types of plant-based milks now available at your local supermarket!

All supermarkets now stock a huge variety of dairy-free products, and the selection continues to grow. It has never been easier to make the switch.

CASHEW MILK

ALMOND MILK

COCONUT MILK

HEMP MILK

SOY MILK

HAZELNUT MILK

RICE MILK

OAT MILK

MAKE YOUR OWN
PLANT-BASED MILK

1 **SOAK NUTS, GRAINS OR SEEDS 12 HOURS OR OVERNIGHT.**
Soaking releases enzyme inhibitors and improves nutrient
digestion/assimilation. Toasting helps, too. It brings out a rich,
"toasty" flavor for milks.

2 **DRAIN THE NUTS/GRAINS/SEEDS AND COMBINE WITH 3 CUPS OF WATER IN A BLENDER.**
Be sure to use fresh water - not your soak water.

3 **ADD YOUR FAVORITE INGREDIENTS TO CREATE THE DESIRED FLAVOR.**
Use dates, fruits, sugar or agave.

4 **BLEND AT HIGH SPEED FOR ONE MINUTE OR UNTIL MIXTURE IS LIQUIFIED.**
A high-speed machine works best.

5 **STRAIN WITH A NUT MILK BAG, IF DESIRED.**
Drape a nut milk bag or cheesecloth over a bowl or large glass.
Pour blended contents through the fabric to strain.

DON'T THROW AWAY THE PULP!

When you make your own non-dairy milk, the process generates leftover pulp. What do you do with this? Most people end up throwing the pulp away and miss out on its benefits. It is rich in protein, minerals and fiber, so why not make use of it?

Below are two examples of how to make use of this nutrient-rich pulp. These feature almond and hazelnut milk, but you can use any plant-milk pulp!

ALMOND PULP CRACKERS

1 In a large bowl, mix 1 cup almond pulp, 3 tbsp olive oil, ¼ tsp salt, 1 tbsp ground flax and 2 tbsp of your favorite dry herbs. **2** Using a rolling pin, flatten the mixture onto parchment paper. **3** Cut the dough into cracker shapes and poke the center of each with a fork. **4** Bake at 350°F (180°C) for 20 minutes, then flip and bake for an additional 20 minutes. Cool completely and serve.

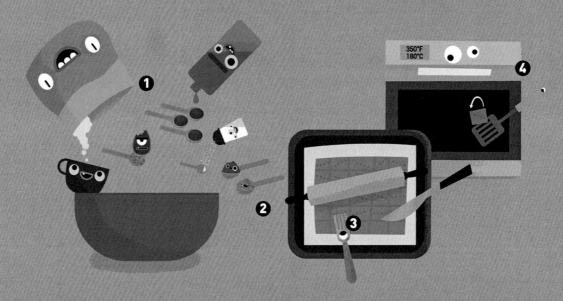

HAZELNUT TRUFFLES

1 Place 1 cup hazelnut pulp, 1 tbsp cocoa powder, 1 tbsp maple syrup and 1 cup pitted dates in a food processor and blend until smooth. **2** Place the mixture in a bowl and add ½ cup chopped hazelnuts. Mix well. **3** Moisten your hands and create dough balls. Serve your delicious truffles!

AQUAFABA

Aquafaba ("water bean") is the common name for the cooking liquid of beans and other legumes such as chickpeas. You may know it as the liquid found in retail cans of beans or the liquid that is left over after cooking your own legumes. It is typically discarded – but it shouldn't be! Aquafaba contains plant nutrients that migrate from the seeds to the water during the cooking process. This unique combination of ingredients gives it a wide spectrum of emulsifying, foaming, binding, gelatinizing, and thickening properties. What's the most common use of aquafaba? It's a great replacement for egg white!

MERINGUES

1 Combine 1 cup of aquafaba and 1 tsp cream of tartar in a bowl. **2** Stir vigorously with a hand whisk until glossy and white. **3** Mix in ½ cup of sugar. **4** Cover baking tray with greaseproof paper and coat paper with vegetable oil. Drop tablespoons of the mixture onto the oiled tray. **5** Bake at 230°F (110°C) for one hour, then check. Meringues should be slightly golden and firm to the touch - not sticky or tacky. If still sticky, continue to bake and check every 10 minutes. **6** When proper texture is achieved, turn off the oven and leave the meringues in the oven to cool - overnight if possible.

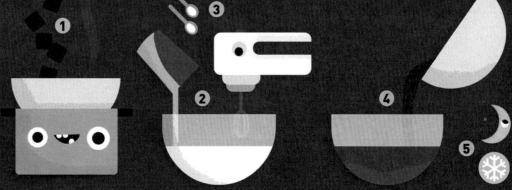

CHOCOLATE MOUSSE

1 Melt 100g of chocolate in a bowl over a pan of simmering water (a bain marie). **2** Remove from heat and allow the chocolate to cool while you prepare the next step. Beat 125 ml of aquafaba with an electric whisk until peaks form. **3** Add 2 tsp stevia. **4** Gently fold in the chocolate and very slightly stir it (make sure the chocolate has cooled first). Use a spatula for this delicate task - don't simply toss it in and whisk it! **5** Chill in fridge overnight.

SAY HOMEMADE CHEESE

RAW CASHEW & ALMOND

1. Place 2 cups raw cashews and 1 cup raw almonds in water and soak overnight (or for at least 4 hours).

2. Place soaked nuts in blender with juice from 1 lemon, 1 cup nutritional yeast, 1 tbsp apple pectin and Himalayan salt, to taste.

3. Blend until mixture has a smooth consistency. You may need to add a little water as you blend.

4. Use a dab of olive oil to grease your hands, then mold the mixture into your desired cheese shape.

5. If desired, sprinkle your favorite spices onto a dish and roll your cheese through them, coating evenly and completely.

6. Place in the refrigerator to chill for at least 3 hours before serving.

JUICE FROM 1 LEMON

1 CUP NUTRITIONAL YEAST

1 TBSP APPLE PECTIN

HIMALAYAN SALT, TO TASTE

COCONUT CREAM CHEESE

2 CUPS CHILLED UNSWEETENED COCONUT CREAM

1 TSP PROBIOTIC POWDER

SALT

ANY FLAVORINGS

1. Using a whisk or mixer, combine 1 tsp probiotic powder and 2 cups unsweetened coconut cream.

2. Place mixture in a cheesecloth pouch, then place pouch in a strainer. (Put the strainer inside a bowl to avoid a mess!) Cover and store in a dark place at room temperature for at least 24 hours. Tip: The longer it sits, the more tangy it will be. Taste occasionally to discover when it reaches the perfect flavor.

3. Remove the cream from the pouch and place in a bowl. Add a pinch of sea salt and any other favorite flavorings you prefer. Cover and chill in the refrigerator for 5 hours or until firm.

CASHEW MOZZAFABA

1. Place ½ cup cashews in water and soak for at least 2 hours.

2. Combine cashews with 1 cup aquafaba and mix until smooth. Add 5 tbsp coconut oil, 2 tbsp cornstarch or tapioca starch, 2 tsp agar agar, 1 tsp lemon juice, 1 tsp nutritional yeast and ½ tsp sea salt or Himalayan salt. Mix thoroughly.

3. Heat in a saucepan until it boils and thickens, stirring constantly.

4. Pour the mixture into a mold and chill for at least 6 hours.

1 CUP AQUAFABA

1 TSP NUTRITIONAL YEAST

5 TBSP COCONUT OIL

1 TSP LEMON JUICE

½ TSP SALT

2 TSP AGAR AGAR

2 TBSP CORNSTARCH OR TAPIOCA STARCH

SOY RICOTTA

1. Bring 2 liters of unsweetened soy milk to a slight boil, then remove from heat.

2. Combine the juice from 3 lemons with ¾ cup hot water. (The heat starts the solidification process.) Pour ⅓ of this mixture into the pan of hot milk and gently stir. Cover and wait 5 minutes. Add just over half of the remaining lemon-water and stir gently. (You should start to see the milk solidify). Cover and wait another 5 minutes. Add the rest of the lemon-water to the milk, stirring gently. Cover and wait for another 15 minutes.

3. Remove liquids by placing the mixture in a cheesecloth and squeezing over a bowl. This moisture-removal will create the hard texture you need for tasty ricotta cheese. Store your ricotta in the refrigerator until you're ready to enjoy!

PLANT-BASED BURGER RECIPES

QUINOA & BLACK BEANS Serves 4

1 serving - Calories: 109 • Protein: 5.5 g • Iron: 1.5 mg • Potassium: 270 mg

1 Coat a skillet with 1 tbsp olive oil and saute 2 garlic cloves, 1 red chili and 1 chopped onion for 5 minutes or until onion is tender. **2** Add ½ tsp ground coriander and 1 tsp smoked paprika and cook for 2-3 more minutes. **3** Place this mixture in a blender with 1 cup drained black beans and a pinch of salt. Blend in short bursts until you achieve a rough paste that is smooth and wet but not runny. **4** Pour into a bowl and add 1 tbsp flour and 5 tbsp cooked quinoa. Mix well. **5** Chill in the fridge for at least one hour. **6** Shape ¼ of the chilled mixture into a ball and place in a heated pan. Use a spatula to press into a patty. Cook for 2-3 minutes on each side, reshaping as needed. When the edges are crispy and dark and the middle is hot, your burger is ready to enjoy!

LENTILS & MUSHROOMS Serves 7

1 serving - Calories: 172 • Protein: 11 g • Iron: 4 mg • Zinc: 2 mg • Fiber: 9 g

1 Coat a skillet with 1 tbsp olive oil and saute 1 sliced red onion for 4-5 minutes, until tender. **2** Add a pinch of salt and 4 cups chopped mushrooms, then cover and cook for 2 minutes, stirring occasionally. **3** Blend the onion mixture with ½ cup rolled oats, 3 cups cooked brown lentils, 3 garlic cloves, 2 tbsp tomato paste, 1 tbsp dried oregano, 2 tbsp tapioca flour and 1 tsp salt in a food processor until smooth. **4** Shape into 6 or 7 equal-sized patties and place on a baking sheet at least one inch apart. **5** Bake at 350°F (180°C) for 10 minutes, then flip and bake 15 more minutes. Serve with your favorite vegan toppings.

CHAPTER 4

PLANNING

How should you plan your meals?
What should you pay attention to?
How awesome am I?

THE MEAL PLANNER PLATE

Here's an example of the daily eating pattern recommended for vegans. It demonstrates the desired relationship between various food groups, expressed as servings per day. These are recommendations, not rules.

GRAINS & STARCHY VEGETABLES 5+ SERVINGS

FRUITS 2+ SERVINGS

SEEDS & NUTS 1-2 SERVINGS

VEGETABLES 4+ SERVINGS

BEANS & LENTILS 3+ SERVINGS

GRAINS & STARCHY VEGETABLES Provide our main source of energy – carbohydrates. Choose whole grains in their most natural form, because they contribute more fiber, vitamins and minerals. • **FRUITS** Contain many vitamins, minerals and powerful antioxidants that protect the body. • **SEEDS AND NUTS** Source of healthy fats and minerals - mainly iron, calcium and zinc. It's better to eat nuts in their natural form rather than salted/candied. • **VEGETABLES** Contain many vitamins, minerals and antioxidants that protect the body. Also have very few calories, so it's good to eat more veggies, both fresh and cooked. • **BEANS & LENTILS** The main source of protein in both quantity and quality. Offer high mineral content, such as iron, zinc and calcium. Contain dietary fiber and phytochemicals that contribute to health. • Drink plenty of water! • Purchase this as an actual plate at **simplehappy.kitchen/plate**.

FIVE COLORS
OF PHYTOCHEMICALS

Phytochemicals are compounds that occur naturally in plants. Many offer health benefits, including antioxidant properties, increased cancer cell death, a healthy digestive system, and protection against environmental toxins. Plant-based foods are a much better source of antioxidants than non-plant foods. Vegetables, spices, herbs, berries, fruits and nuts top the charts for antioxidant content. Each color represents a family of phytochemicals. By eating foods from every color, you can enjoy the benefits of each family.

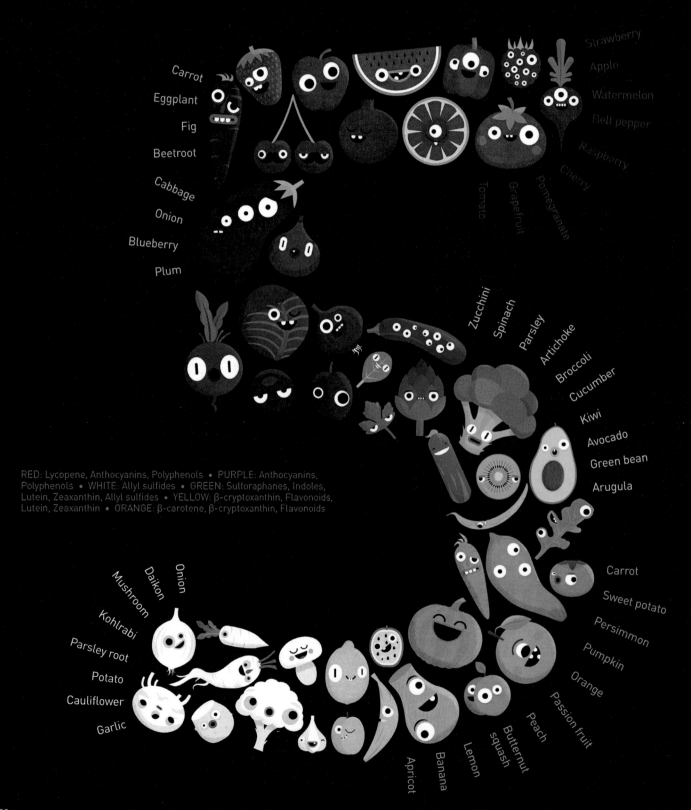

RED: Lycopene, Anthocyanins, Polyphenols • PURPLE: Anthocyanins, Polyphenols • WHITE: Allyl sulfides • GREEN: Sulforaphanes, Indoles, Lutein, Zeaxanthin, Allyl sulfides • YELLOW: β-cryptoxanthin, Flavonoids, Lutein, Zeaxanthin • ORANGE: β-carotene, β-cryptoxanthin, Flavonoids

6 HEALTHY SMOOTHIE IDEAS

Choose your favorite, put all ingredients in a blender and blend until smooth! Each serves 3.

POST WORKOUT

- 3 medium ripe bananas
- 3 tbsp cocoa powder
- 4 tbsp 100% peanut butter
- 2 cups soy milk

Rich in zinc and potassium.
1 serving: Calories: 326 • Protein: 12 g
• Iron: 1 mg • Calcium: 100 mg •
Zinc: 3.5 mg • Potassium: 550 mg

RED REFRESH

- 3¾ cups fresh strawberries
- 1½ cup ice cubes
- 1½ cup unsweetened non-dairy milk

Rich in calcium and antioxidants.
1 serving: Calories: 120 • Protein: 5.5 g
• Iron: 1 mg • Calcium: 180 mg •
Vitamin C: 110 mg

VEG BLAST

- 1 cup chopped kale (without ribs)
- 1 cored & chopped apple
- 1 cup spinach
- ¼ cup orange juice
- ¼ cup carrot juice
- 5 small frozen broccoli florets
- 1 frozen sliced banana

**Low in calories and fat, rich in folic acid and
antioxidants important for vision.**
1 serving: Calories: 105 • Protein: 3 g •
Iron: 1 mg • Calcium: 70 mg • Folate: 84 mcg
• Vitamin C: 50 mg

COCOA GO-GO

- 3 tbsp chia seeds
- 2 tbsp cocoa powder
- 1 cup cooked sweet potato
- 3 frozen sliced bananas
- 3 cups unsweetened non-dairy milk

Rich in calcium and vitamin A.
1 serving: Calories: 370 • Protein: 13 g •
Iron: 2 mg • Calcium: 230 mg

BLIND DATE

- 2 medium ripe bananas
- 5 dates
- 2 cups frozen raspberries
- 2 cups water
- 1 tbsp ground flax seeds

Rich in potassium and dietary fiber.
1 serving: Calories: 166 • Protein: 3 g •
Iron: 1.5 mg • Fiber: 10 g •
Potassium: 520 mg

BERRY BLEND

- A small piece of peeled ginger
- 3½ cups water
- 3 cups spinach
- 3 dates
- 3 cups frozen strawberries
- 1 cup frozen wild blueberries
- ⅔ cup rolled oats
- 4 tbsp almond butter

**Rich in iron, magnesium and strong
antioxidants. 1 serving:** Calories: 370 •
Protein: 12 g • Iron: 5 mg • Calcium: 157 mg
• Fiber: 12 g • Magnesium: 167 mg

SAMPLE DAILY MENU CHECKLIST

BEING A VEGAN IS EASY! USE THIS MENU ORGANIZER TO APPLY THE BASICS OF A HEALTHY PLANT-BASED DIET.

Plan at least two meals that are ⅓ legumes, ⅓ grains, and ⅓ vegetables.

Include at least 1 serving of fruit.

Make sure all of your main meals include fresh vegetables.

Include at least 1 serving of nuts or seeds.

Choose a calcium-enriched plant milk substitute.

Take your B12 supplement.

If you have any health issues, consult your healthcare provider about dietary supplements and fortified food intake.

CHALLENGE YOURSELF

DO YOU THINK YOU CAN TAKE ON THESE CHALLENGES?

Pick 4 iron-rich foods and include them in different meals.

Pick 4 calcium-rich foods and include them in different meals.

Replace your regular salt with iodized salt.

Eat 4 or more colors of fruits and vegetables.

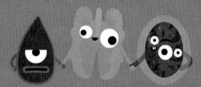

Include 1-2 servings of omega-3-rich seeds and nuts.

Sprout your beans.

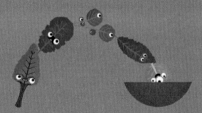

Add green leaves to your cooked meal or salad.

Wait at least half an hour after a meal before drinking coffee or tea.

Replace one of your meals with a large bean-filled salad.

For the entire day, only eat food you prepared yourself.

Drink plenty of water.

Treat yourself with a green smoothie.

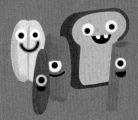

Use whole-wheat bread, pasta, flour, and cereals.

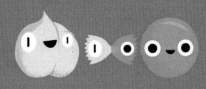

Use pastas that are made of legume flours instead of wheat noodles.

Use nutrient-rich spreads for your sandwich, such as whole tahini, natural peanut butter, or homemade bean spreads.

BUDGET-FRIENDLY MEAL PLAN

When you're trying to stick to a budget, meal planning and cooking at home can help you save some serious cash. Use this meal planner to create affordable, delicious, easy-to-make meals with low-cost, easy-to-find ingredients. **Choose one option from each category**, or use these ideas as inspiration to create similar menus.

BREAKFAST

Oat porridge

Chia pudding + fruit

Soy yogurt + fruit + nuts

Whole-grain cereals + soy milk + fruit

MID-MORNING SNACK

Whole-wheat bread sandwich with hummus, tahini or peanut butter + vegetables

Nuts + fruit

LUNCH

Pasta in Bolognese tomato sauce (Lentils- or Soya granules-based)

Majadara (50% lentils, 50% rice or other grain)

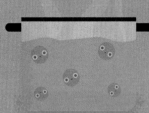

Red lentil soup

Couscous with vegetables and chickpeas

MID-AFTERNOON SNACK

Handful of roasted peanuts or any other roasted legume

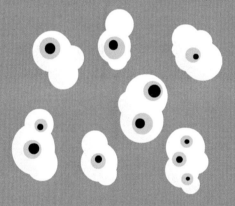

Popcorn (homemade in a pot)

DINNER

Large vegetable salad + legumes + whole-wheat bread slice

Tabbouleh salad

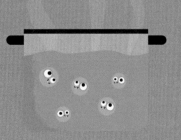

Pea soup

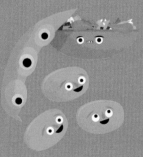

Edamame bowl + vegetable salad

8 GREAT KITCHEN HACKS

MAKE CRYSTAL-CLEAR ICE CUBES

Boil water twice. Cool until manageable, then pour into an ice cube tray for freezing. You'll get crystal-clear cubes, and you'll get them faster by starting with hot water. Strange, but it works!

SLICE CHERRY TOMATOES

Place tomatoes of equal height on a plate and cover with a matching plate. Press down on the top plate and slide a knife between the plates to cut the tomatoes. Works with grapes too!

REFRESH YOUR BREAD

Enjoy a moist, like-new loaf! Spray your day-old crusty bread with water and place it in the oven for about 6 minutes at 300°F (150°C).

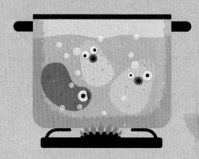

SKIP THE POTATO PEELER

Boil potatoes with the skin on. When they're tender, immediately transfer them to ice water. The skin will fall right off!

MAKE VEGETABLE BROTH FROM KITCHEN SCRAPS

Any time you chop carrots, onions, celery, mushrooms or other vegetables, toss the scraps in a gallon freezer bag. When the bag is full, place the scraps in a stockpot full of water and bring the mixture to a boil. Cover partially and simmer for about an hour.

SLICE SOFT CAKES WITH FLOSS

While holding the floss taut, press it down into the cake to make clean, precise cuts. To prevent icing smears, pull the floss out from the side rather than up through the top. Oh, and slice with fresh floss only - not used! *Eww!*

PEEL GARLIC IN A FLASH

Place garlic cloves in a bowl with a lid and shake it vigorously. When you're done, you'll have naked garlic.

PEEL GINGER WITH A SPOON

With the ginger in one hand, use the other hand to scrape off the peel with a spoon. The peel comes off easily - even better than with a vegetable peeler or knife!

EASY-TO-MAKE HEALTHY SNACKS

CRUNCHY ROASTED GREEN PEAS **SERVES 4**

1 Thaw 2 cups of frozen green peas. **2** Blot the peas with a paper towel to remove as much moisture as possible. **3** Place peas in a bowl and add 1 tsp olive oil and ½ tsp salt. Stir to coat evenly. **4** Spread peas on a baking sheet lined with parchment paper. **5** Bake for 30 minutes at 350°F (180°C). Every 10 minutes, shake the baking sheet a little to make sure the peas cook evenly. **6** Cool and serve.

BAKED KALE CHIPS **SERVES 6**

1 Using a knife or kitchen shears, carefully remove kale leaves from the thick stems. **2** Tear the kale into bite-size pieces and wash. **3** Use a salad spinner to dry the kale. **4** Lightly coat the kale with olive oil and add a dash of seasoning salt. **5** Bake for about 12 minutes at 350°F (180°C) - until edges are browned.

SESAME NORI CHIPS **SERVES 6**

1 Place 6 sheets of nori shiny-side up and lightly brush with water. Press a second sheet on top, repeating until all sheets are paired. **2** Cut the nori into chip-size strips. **3** Arrange strips in a single layer on baking sheets. Brush the tops of the strips with sesame oil. **4** Place on the middle oven rack and bake for 15 minutes at 275°F (135°C). For the best crunchy taste, allow to cool before munching.

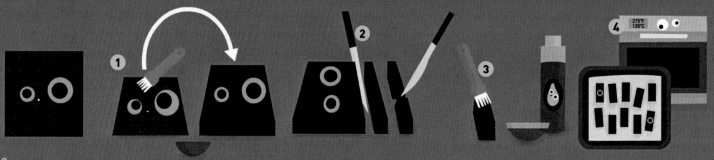

SALT 'N SOUR EDAMAME

1 Steam or boil edamame for 5 minutes (Steaming is the preferred method). **2** Drain. **3** Lightly coat edamame with lemon juice and olive oil, then salt.

TAHINI & ALMOND COOKIES `MAKES 15-20 COOKIES`

1 Mix ¼ cup tahini with ¼ cup maple syrup. **2** Add 1½ cups almond flour and some chopped almonds. **3** Roll the mixture into small balls of dough and place on baking sheet lined with parchment paper. **4** Bake at 350°F (180°C) for 10 minutes. **5** Cool and serve.

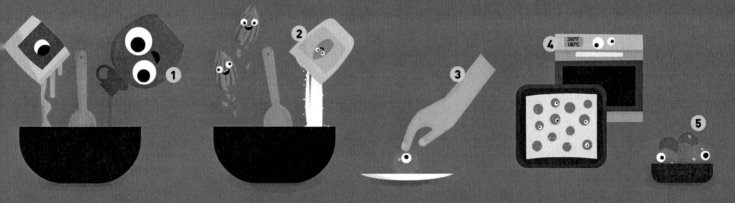

GRANOLA BARS `MAKES 15-20 BARS`

1 Place 1 cup pitted dates in a food processor and blend for one minute. **2** In a large bowl, mix blended dates with 1½ cups rolled oats and 1 cup chopped almonds. **3** In a saucepan, heat ¼ cup maple syrup and ¼ cup unsweetened peanut butter. **4** Combine hot mixture with oats and place in a flat baking dish. **5** Cover and chill in fridge for 30 minutes or until firm. **6** Cut into serving-size bars and place in an airtight container to keep for up to three days.

 # HEALTHY COOKING TIPS

YOU DON'T HAVE TO GIVE UP YOUR FAVORITE FOODS TO EAT HEALTHY.
SIMPLY ADAPT YOUR FAVORITE RECIPES TO CREATE HEALTHIER ALTERNATIVES.

Swap out some of your white flour for whole wheat
or spelt. They have more fiber and minerals.

Invest in a high-quality, non-stick frying pan.
You'll need less oil.

Use sprouted beans. Nutrient absorption
is better and digestion is easier.

Lower your sodium intake by using a variety of
herbs and spices for flavoring instead of salt.

Choose boiling or baking over frying.
This allows you to use less oil.

Use a colander to steam your veggies over
simmering water. This reduces vitamin
and mineral loss to cooking water.

SALT REDUCTION

Table salt, or common salt, is composed of two minerals: sodium and chloride (NaCl). This crystal-like compound is found abundantly in nature and is used to flavor and preserve food.

SODIUM   SODIUM CHLORIDE (SALT)   CHLORIDE

Sodium is an essential mineral, but we tend to eat way too much of it! Too much sodium can elevate blood pressure, increase risk for heart attack and stroke, and can be bad for your bones and kidneys.

The Recommended Dietary Allowance (RDA) for sodium is less than 2,400 mg. That's equal to about one teaspoon of salt!

When cooking, try to gradually lower the amount of salt you use.

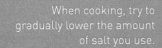

Try flavoring with a variety of fresh and dried herbs, vegetables, and spices and unsalted seasonings.

Many people think the salt shaker is the main culprit of an over-salted diet. This isn't true. The fact is, around three-fourths of dietary sodium comes from processed and restaurant foods. Only about a tenth of salt consumption comes from the salt we add to food while cooking or eating. To cut down on your salt intake, simply eat more home-made foods.

When buying food products, always read labels. Look for options with lower sodium contents. The FDA considers 5% DV (120 mg) or less to be low in sodium. 20% DV (480 mg) or more is considered high in sodium.

If you eat out, order menu items that are less processed. If your selection comes with dressing or sauce, ask for this on the side, then only use a small portion of it.

SUPER★FOODS

No precise, formal definition exists for "superfoods." The common claim is that these foods are more nutritious than other foods and therefore offer medicinal properties. However, this has not been scientifically proven. It is claimed that they have significant advantages, especially in antioxidant content, over the usual foods we know. Because of this, some exotic superfoods are sold at inflated prices and can't be found in regular supermarkets.

The fact is, we can find many antioxidants in our daily foods. Some even contain more antioxidants than the so-called superfoods.

Does this mean you shouldn't eat products labeled "Superfood?" No. You can include them in your menu, but you don't need to do it at the expense of the regular vegetables, fruits, seeds, and legumes you already know and love.

PURPLE GRAPES
Top source of antioxidants.

Protects from cell damage.

PUMPKIN SEEDS
Top source of zinc.

Boosts immune system and helps heal wounds.

KALE
Top source of lutein and zeaxanthin.

Protects and improves eyesight.

YELLOW BELL PEPPER
Top source of vitamin C.

Increases plant iron absorption.

SOY
Top source of high quality protein, rich in iron, calcium, and hytochemicals. Contributes health-essential nutrients.

CHIA SEEDS
Top source of omega-3.

Promotes a healthy lipid profile.

SWEET POTATO
Top source of beta-carotene.

Protects the skin and surface of the eye for healthy vision.

TAHINI
Top source of calcium.

Promotes bone health.

WATERMELON
Top source of lycopene.

Acts as a strong antioxidant agent.

RAW FOOD

Like veganism, raw veganism is defined in a variety of ways. The common ground among definitions is an avoidance of all animal products and cooked foods. Some raw vegans may even avoid sprouted beans and grains and limit or avoid consumption of nuts and seeds. The diet varies from 50% to 100% raw foods.

Adherents to a raw-food diet believe it is the most natural eating pattern for humans because it preserves the true value of food. The premise for consuming such a diet is not yet scientifically supported. Although cooking may destroy some of the nutrients in foods, heat also improves their digestibility, destroys natural mineral inhibitors, and helps improve absorption of protein and iron. Still, a raw vegan diet can be adequate for adults if sprouted beans and grains are used in sufficient quantities. It is not recommended for babies and children.

48°C
118°F

NON-RAW

RAW

TRY THESE EASY RAW RECIPES

CARROT SOUP

Place in a blender: a pinch of salt, 1 cup carrot juice, 1 tsp curry powder, 1 tsp lime juice, and ½ avocado, chopped. Blend on medium speed until smooth. Serves 1.

PASTA WITH PUMPKIN SEEDS

Use a spiral slicer to make zucchini noodles (zoodles) from 2 zucchinis. To create the sauce, mix 1 pitted, chopped date, ¼ cup water, 3 tbsp nutritional yeast, ¼ cup fresh basil leaves, ⅓ cup pumpkin seeds and 1 chopped garlic clove. Combine zoodles with sauce. Serves 1.

CHOCOLATE & PEANUT BUTTER FUDGE

In a high-speed blender, combine 1 cup unsalted peanut butter, 2 cups cacao powder, 1 cup coconut oil, 1 cup pitted dates, and a pinch of salt until well blended. Spread the mixture in a single, even layer in the bottom of a flat container. Chill for 2 hours. Makes about 16 one-inch pieces.

GLUTEN & CELIAC DISEASE

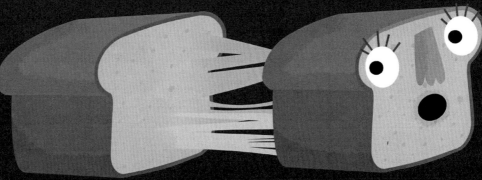

Gluten is the protein found in wheat, (wheat berries, durum, emmer, semolina, spelt, farina, farro, graham, kamut, khorasan wheat and einkorn), rye, barley and triticale.

When flour is mixed with water, gluten proteins form a sticky substance that has a glue-like consistency. This makes the dough elastic and gives bread the ability to rise when baked. The name glu-ten is derived from this glue-like property of wet dough. Don't worry – that doesn't mean the dough will stick to your digestive tract.

Celiac disease is a serious autoimmune disorder. It is estimated that 0.5%-1% of the world population has this condition. When people with celiac disease eat gluten, their body's immune system attacks the small intestine, causing damage to its structure and a reduction in nutrient absorption.

Non-celiac gluten sensitivity is present when symptoms similar to celiac disease occur but the immune system is not involved and there is no damage to the intestine.

A life-long gluten-free diet is the only accepted treatment for celiac disease, as it requires elimination of these proteins. Oat may be acceptable if not contaminated by wheat products.

Gluten-free products are often low in B vitamins, calcium, vitamin D, iron, zinc, magnesium, and fiber, so it is essential to include sources of these nutrients when on a gluten-free diet. Due to the nutritional risks associated with this diet, the American Gastroenterological Association recommends that a person with celiac disease meet with a registered dietitian on a regular basis. While mandatory for those with celiac disease, a gluten-free diet may also benefit those who suffer from other kinds of abdominal discomfort. However, despite its increased popularity in recent years, people with no gluten sensitivity of any kind won't necessarily benefit from sticking to a gluten-free diet.

FERMENTING VEGETABLES

Fermentation is an ancient process dating back thousands of years. It is the means by which bread, wine, beer, and cheese are made. Fermentation is essentially a sort of pre-digestion that takes place when naturally present bacteria in foods, such as Lactobacillus bacteria, begin breaking down food compounds. As these bacteria divide, they produce substances like lactic acid, which halts the growth of bad or putrefying bacteria. This lactic acid preserves the food and prevents it from rotting. Lactic acid is responsible for the sour taste that is inherent to fermented foods. It also promotes the growth of healthy bacteria already in the gut and increases levels of some B vitamins. Lactic acid further aids digestion by increasing mineral absorption through the breakdown of inhibitors, like phytate.

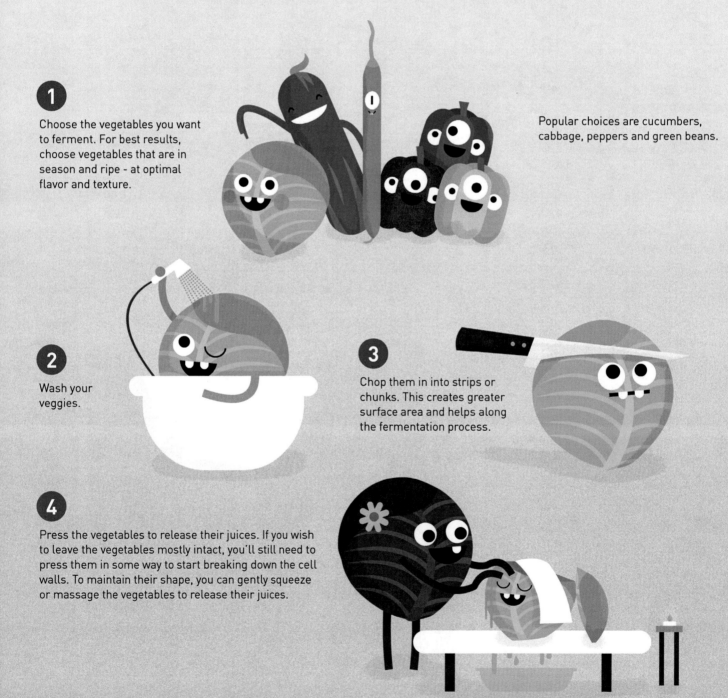

1

Choose the vegetables you want to ferment. For best results, choose vegetables that are in season and ripe - at optimal flavor and texture.

Popular choices are cucumbers, cabbage, peppers and green beans.

2

Wash your veggies.

3

Chop them in into strips or chunks. This creates greater surface area and helps along the fermentation process.

4

Press the vegetables to release their juices. If you wish to leave the vegetables mostly intact, you'll still need to press them in some way to start breaking down the cell walls. To maintain their shape, you can gently squeeze or massage the vegetables to release their juices.

5

Add sea salt, mixing it with the vegetables and juice. The standard amount of salt to add is 3 tbsp per 5 pounds (2¼ kg) of vegetables. If you're on a low sodium diet, it's fine to add salt to taste. You can use a starter culture as well.

6

Place the mixture in your chosen container. Be sure to leave 3 inches (7.6 cm) or so of empty space at the top of the container. Press the vegetables down to the bottom so that the juice rises to cover the solid parts. If there isn't enough juice to cover the vegetables, top it off with water.

7

To ferment, the vegetables must be weighted under the liquid, so place a weight inside the container. Cover the container with a lid, Store at room temperature in a clean, dry area. The vegetables will immediately begin to break down and ferment.

8

Taste the vegetables every day. There's no precise moment at which a ferment is "ready" - it's all a matter of taste. After just a day or two, the mixture will develop a tang. Keep tasting it every day until it reaches the level of tartness you want.

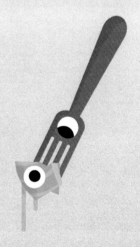

9

To preserve, transfer your fermenting vegetables to a cooler temperature. Place the container in the cellar or in your refrigerator. This will slow down the fermentation process, allowing you to keep the food for several months. As the vegetables continue to ferment, their flavor will deepen. Keep tasting the ferment every few weeks, and eat it as soon as it tastes the way you want it to.

This easy-peasy process allows you to enjoy the special taste and nutritional value of fermented vegetables. Almost any vegetable can be fermented, and fermenting farm-fresh produce is a great way to provide good nutrition year-round!

CHAPTER 5:

WHO

...ARE THE NUTRIENTS AND WHERE ARE THEY?

Protein, calcium, iron, vitamins, minerals, dietary fiber. Why do we need all these, and how can we be sure to find them? Let me show you!

PLAIN-BASED PROTEIN SOURCES

SOYBEANS
31 g/cup

EDAMAME
19 g/cup

LENTILS
18 g/cup

TOFU
15 g/100g (3.5 oz)

RED BEANS
15 g/cup

CHICKPEAS
15 g/cup

LIMA BEANS
15 g/cup

PEAS
8 g/cup

QUINOA (COOKED)
8 g/cup

SOY MILK
7 g/cup

OATS
6 g/3 tbsp

LENTIL FLOUR
6 g/tbsp

SPINACH (COOKED)
4 g/0.5 cup

PUMPKIN SEEDS
4 g/tbsp

PEANUT BUTTER
4 g/tbsp

WHOLE WHEAT BREAD
4 g/slice

FLAXSEEDS (GROUND)
3 g/2 tbsp

WHOLE SEED TAHINI
3 g/tbsp

POTATO (COOKED)
3 g/medium unit

ALMONDS
2.5 g/9 units

PISTACHIOS
2 g/15 units

CHIA SEEDS
2 g/tbsp

CASHEWS
2 g/6 units

HAZELNUTS
2 g/7 units

WALNUTS
2 g/5 halves

(Protein content for a serving size of cooked legumes)

PROTEIN

YOU NEED IT TO MAKE...

Muscle on bones

Blood

Connective Tissues

Enzymes

Antibodies

Hair

Protein is essential to good health. The Greek origin of the word reflects protein's top-shelf status in human nutrition. It stems from "protos", meaning "first."

The body uses 20 building blocks called amino acids to build protein.

Protein requirements vary. The Recommended Dietary Allowance (RDA) for protein is a modest 0.8 grams of protein per kilogram of body weight. For example, a woman who weighs 60 kg (about 130 lbs) needs 48 g of protein each day, and a man who weighs 80 kg (about 175 pounds) needs 64 g per day. However, protein requirements rise when a person is physically active.

Babies and kids have different needs. If you have a special condition (illness, pregnancy, lactating, or suffer from obesity or are underweight), you should consult with your healthcare provider to determine the amount of protein that is right for you.

The terms "complete protein" and "incomplete protein" can be misleading. If your caloric intake is sufficient, eating a variety of plant protein sources throughout the day ensures you will get adequate levels of all essential amino acids. A regular diet that includes legumes and soy products will provide proper protein values and quality, as well as other essential nutrients.

132 lbs (60 KG) = 48 g Protein/day

Keep in mind, when it comes to protein, quantity isn't the most important factor. Look for quality. Some proteins are packed with harmful components, such as saturated fat and added salt (like most types of meat). Other proteins are loaded with beneficial ingredients, such as fiber, vitamins, minerals, and antioxidants. To get the healthiest combination, choose unprocessed plant-based sources of protein.

As you plan your vegan diet, remember that protein is an important component, but there is no need to overdo it. A healthy balance is necessary, since consuming too much protein can increase the risk of various diseases.

A PROTEIN-RICH MEAL PLAN

It's very easy to meet the recommendations for protein. Here's an example of a daily meal plan that provides 107 grams of protein! Total calories: 1,851.

BREAKFAST

	Protein	Calories
Scrambled tofu (150 g)	23	225
Salad (3 vegetables)	2	60
Avocado (¼ unit)	1	80
Rice cracker (2 units)	2	70
Total	**28**	**435**

MID-MORNING

	Protein	Calories
Chia pudding		
Chia seeds (2 tbsp)	4	116
Soy milk (1 cup)	7	113
Fruit (1 unit)	1	60
Total	**12**	**289**

LUNCH

	Protein	Calories
Legume pasta (1 cup)	22	173
Tomato & mushroom sauce	4	72
Vegetables (3 units)	2	60
Total	**28**	**305**

MID-AFTERNOON

	Protein	Calories
Whole wheat bread (2 slices)	6	130
Peanut butter (2 tbsp)	8	188
Jam (1 tsp)	0	25
Total	**14**	**343**

DINNER

	Protein	Calories
Bean burger patty (1 unit)	16	225
Bun (1 unit)	3	110
Salad (3 vegetables)	2	60
Pumpkin seeds (1 tbsp)	4	84
Total	**25**	**479**

These suggestions offer a balanced daily menu. Emphasis is placed on protein, but this plan supplies all required nutrients.

TIPS TO KEEP YOUR PROTEIN LEVEL HAPPY

Load up on legumes in your daily menu. Make sure at least two of your meals are made up of 50% legumes.

Snack on handfuls of nuts and seeds throughout the day.

Choose protein-rich spreads or plant-based alternatives for your sandwiches, such as peanut butter, hummus or tofu.

WHOLE SEED TAHINI

PEANUT BUTTER

HUMMUS

Replace 50% of your daily grain intake with whole grains. Use whole wheat bread, whole grain rice, whole wheat pasta and oats.

SOY MILK

Turn to unsweetened soy milk for your main milk substitute.

PLANT-BASED
CALCIUM SOURCES

SOY MILK (ENRICHED)
290 mg/cup

TOFU
250 mg/100 g (3.5 oz)

SOYBEANS
175 mg/cup

WHITE BEANS
160 mg/cup

SPINACH (COOKED)
145 mg/0.5 cup

WHOLE SEED TAHINI
120 mg/tbsp

EDAMAME
100 mg/cup

CHICKPEAS
80 mg/cup

CHIA SEEDS
75 mg/tbsp

ORANGE
65 mg/unit

ADZUKI BEANS
65 mg/cup

BROCCOLI
60 mg/cup

OKRA
60 mg/0.5 cup

SNAP BEANS
55 mg/cup

FIG
40 mg/2 units

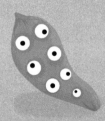

SWEET POTATO (COOKED)
40 mg/medium unit

PARSLEY (CHOPPED)
40 mg/0.5 cup

CARROT
40 mg/medium unit

PUMPKIN (MASHED)
40 mg/cup

CABBAGE
35 mg/cup

ALMONDS
30 mg/9 nuts

QUINOA (COOKED)
30 mg/cup

TOMATO
30 mg/2 units

ARUGULA
30 mg/cup

BRAZIL NUTS
25 mg/3 nuts

(Calcium content for a serving size of cooked legumes)

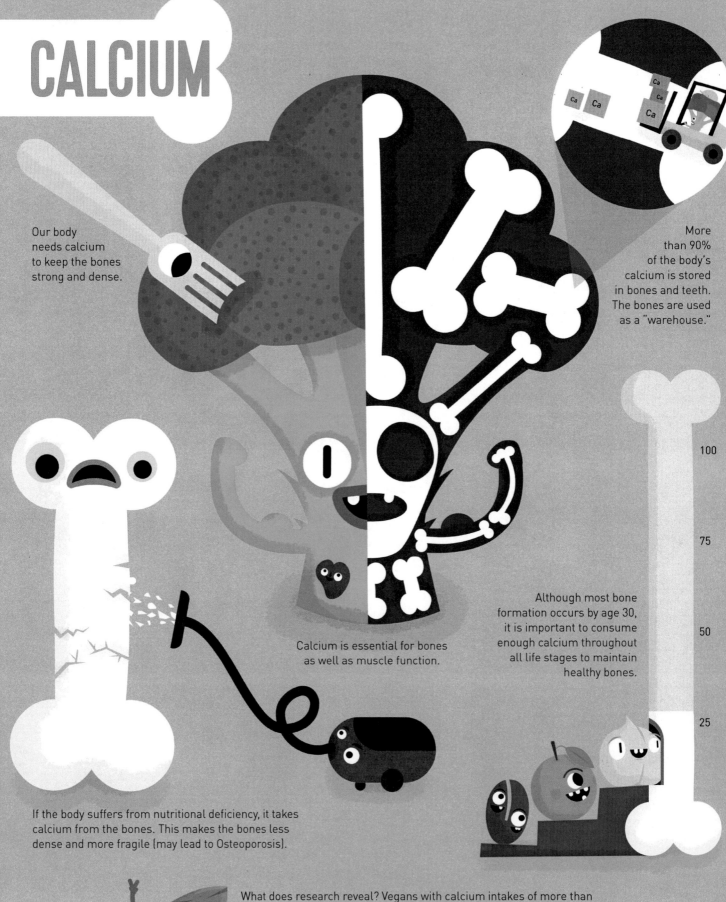

CALCIUM

Our body needs calcium to keep the bones strong and dense.

More than 90% of the body's calcium is stored in bones and teeth. The bones are used as a "warehouse."

Calcium is essential for bones as well as muscle function.

Although most bone formation occurs by age 30, it is important to consume enough calcium throughout all life stages to maintain healthy bones.

100

75

50

25

If the body suffers from nutritional deficiency, it takes calcium from the bones. This makes the bones less dense and more fragile (may lead to Osteoporosis).

What does research reveal? Vegans with calcium intakes of more than 525 mg/day experienced no difference in fracture risk, compared to omnivores and vegetarians. Additionally, greater intake of legumes and meat substitutes reduced risk of hip fracture and provided greater protection than that of meat.

The content of calcium in a meal affects its absorption, so it's better to eat calcium-rich foods throughout the day rather than have them all in one meal.

Natural compounds like phytate, oxalate and fiber that are found in plant foods may interfere with calcium absorption. Despite this, calcium absorption from plant foods is high, with the exception of high-oxalate vegetables like spinach, Swiss chard, beet greens, and rhubarb.

Good sources of calcium include soy products and some legumes, seeds, and nuts. Leafy green vegetables (like turnip greens and kale) and cruciferous vegetables (like cabbage and broccoli) contain less calcium, but they make up for it with high absorption rates. Calcium-fortified products like orange juice, cereals, and plant-based milks can also help you reach the recommended calcium intake.

Vitamin D is crucial for the absorption of calcium, so maintain healthy levels with rich vitamin D sources and supplements. Keep track of your vitamin D levels by maintaining a blood-test routine.

WHAT'S THE CALCIUM RECOMMENDED DAILY ALLOWANCE?

700 mg
Children 1-3

1,000 mg
Children 4-8,
Female 19-50, Male 19-70

1,200 mg
Female 51+,
Male 71+

1,300 mg
Children 9-18

Recommendations from health organizations vary greatly, ranging from 500-700 mg up to 1,000 mg per day, so there seems to be a lack of consensus on the exact amount of calcium we need. Values listed here are the recommendations from the Institute of Medicine.

GOOD FOR YOUR BONES

Vitamin D

Physical exercise

Magnesium

Antioxidants

Potassium

Protein

Vitamin C

Vitamin K

BAD FOR YOUR BONES

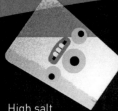
High salt intake

Smoking

High protein intake

A CALCIUM-RICH MEAL PLAN

Getting enough calcium in your vegan diet? It's easy peasy! Here's a sample daily meal plan that provides 1,283 mg of calcium. Total calories: 1,973.

BREAKFAST

	Calcium	Calories
Vegan hotdog	0	50
Tofu scramble (50 g)	125	75
White bean (1 cup) in tomato sauce (½ cup)	177	250
Grilled tomatoes (1 cup)	14	22
Grilled mushrooms (1 cup)	4	35
Total	**320**	**432**

English breakfast!

MID-MORNING

	Calcium	Calories
Orange (1 unit)	65	70
Almonds (9 units)	30	63
Total	**95**	**133**

LUNCH

	Calcium	Calories
5 Broccoli & red lentil patties	110	345
Whole seed tahini (2 tbsp)	240	190
Vegetables (3 units)	30	60
Total	**380**	**595**

MID-AFTERNOON

	Calcium	Calories
Edamame (1 cup)	100	188
Vegetables (2 units)	20	40
Total	**120**	**228**

DINNER

	Calcium	Calories
Homemade hummus with whole seed tahini (1 cup)	320	460
Whole grain bread (1 slice)	18	65
Vegetables (3 units)	30	60
Total	**368**	**585**

These suggestions offer a balanced daily menu. Emphasis is placed on calcium, but this plan supplies all required nutrients.

PLANT-BASED
IRON SOURCES

SOYBEANS
8.5 mg/cup

WHITE BEANS
6.5 mg/cup

GREEN LENTILS
6 mg/cup

AMARANTH (COOKED)
5 mg/cup

CHICKPEAS
4.5 mg/cup

EDAMAME
3.5 mg/cup

MUNG BEANS
3 mg/cup

PEAS
2.5 mg/cup

TOFU
2.5 mg/100g (3.5 oz)

MUSHROOMS (COOKED)
2.5 mg/cup

QUINOA (COOKED)
2.5 mg/cup

SPINACH (COOKED)
2 mg/0.5 cup

BEETROOT (COOKED)
1.5 mg/cup

WHOLE WHEAT BREAD
1.5 mg/slice

PUMPKIN (MASHED)
2.5 mg/cup

PARSLEY (CHOPPED)
2 mg/0.5 cup

WHOLE SEED TAHINI
1 mg/tbsp

OATS
1.5 mg/3 tbsp

CHIA SEEDS
1 mg/tbsp

KALE (CHOPPED)
1 mg/cup

GOJI BERRIES
1 mg/3 tbsp

POTATO (UNPEELED)
0.5 mg/medium unit, cooked

RED BELL PEPPER
0.5 mg/medium unit

SUNFLOWER SEEDS
0.5 mg/tbsp

ORANGE
0.5 mg/medium unit

(Iron content for a serving size of cooked legumes)

IRON

Iron is an essential mineral for a healthy immune system. It's also found in key enzymes. We need iron to transfer oxygen between body tissues. Most iron in our body is found in two proteins that carry oxygen: hemoglobin in our blood cells and myoglobin in muscle.

Dietary iron exists as heme iron, which is found in animal foods, and as non-heme iron, which is found in both animal and plant foods. Heme iron is absorbed more easily than non-heme iron. Non-heme iron absorption can vary greatly, depending on meal composition and the individual's iron status.

RECOMMENDED DIETARY ALLOWANCES (RDAs)

Vegans generally consume as much iron as omnivores. Despite that, the iron stores (ferritin) of vegans are typically below those of nonvegans. Lower serum ferritin levels may be an advantage, because elevated serum ferritin levels have independently been associated with the risk of developing metabolic syndrome.

It is worth mentioning that women in their reproductive years are more likely to suffer from iron deficiency due to losses during menstruation. Because of this, they have a much higher recommended iron-intake goal than other groups.

0-6 months		7-12 months		1-3 years		4-8 years		9-13 years		14-18 years		19-50 years		51+ years	
F	M	F	M	F	M	F	M	F	M	F	M	F	M	F	M
0.27* mg	0.27* mg	11 mg	11 mg	7 mg	7 mg	10 mg	10 mg	8 mg	8 mg	15 mg	11 mg	18 mg	8 mg	8 mg	8 mg

* Adequate Intake (AI)

WAYS TO INCREASE IRON ABSORPTION

Bioavailability of non-heme iron is impacted by the ratio of inhibitors and enhancers present. Inhibitors include phytates and polyphenolics. Enhancers include vitamin C, citric acid and other organic acids. We now know that individuals can adapt and absorb non-heme iron more effectively over time.

Avoid consuming coffee, tea or chocolate for half an hour before or after a meal, since these can interfere with iron absorption and cause iron absorption disorder.

Soak or sprout legumes before cooking/eating. This rids the legumes of some iron absorption inhibitors and makes the iron content more available to our digestive system.

Iron and calcium can interfere with each other's absorption. Since the overall effect is minimal, you don't have to worry about separating foods that contain iron and calcium. However, if you take a calcium or iron supplement, you should do so separately from your meal.

Add a fresh fruit or vegetable that is high in vitamin C content to each meal, especially meals which contain iron-rich foods. This will aid in iron absorption.

AN IRON-RICH MEAL PLAN

Getting enough iron is easy! Here's an example of a daily meal plan
that provides 27.5 mg of iron! Total calories: 2,011.

BREAKFAST

	Iron	Calories
Oats (6 tbsp)	3.2	272
Banana (1 unit)	0.3	105
Almonds (10 units)	0.5	70
Total	**4**	**447**

MID-MORNING

	Iron	Calories
A handful of roasted soybeans	2	280
A handful of cherry tomatoes	0.5	20
Total	**2.5**	**300**

LUNCH

	Iron	Calories
Lentils and parsley patties (4 units)	7.7	236
Cooked quinoa (½ cup) and mushrooms (½ cup)	2.7	133
Vegetables (3 units)	1	60
Total	**11.4**	**429**

MID-AFTERNOON

	Iron	Calories
Large whole-wheat pita pocket	2	168
Hummus (3 tbsp)	0.7	81
Vegetable (1 unit)	0.3	20
Total	**3**	**269**

DINNER

	Iron	Calories
Red lentils omelet (2 heaping tbsp lentil flour)	3.8	291
Whole wheat bread (1 slice)	0.8	80
Whole seed tahini (1 tbsp)	1	135
Vegetables (3 units)	1	60
Total	**6.6**	**566**

These suggestions offer a balanced daily menu. Emphasis is placed on iron, but this plan supplies all required nutrients.

VITAMINS

WATER SOLUBLE VITAMINS

These vitamins don't need fat to be digested and are generally not stored in the body.

Iron

VITAMIN C

This vitamin is a well-known antioxidant. When taken with a meal, it helps increase mineral absorption. Vitamin C is also important in the formation of collagen, which is one of the most common types of protein in the body. Fresh fruits and vegetables are a rich source of vitamin C; however, the amount drops significantly when they are cooked.

B COMPLEX VITAMINS

This group of vitamins works together to help enzymes in our body work effectively. They are essential for the metabolism of carbohydrates, fats and proteins and are also involved in energy production. B complex vitamins are present in various forms in beans, grains, and cereals and in some vegetables, fruits, nuts, and seeds. Enriched cereals are one of the best sources for B complex vitamins, and nutritional yeast contains the highest concentration of all.

FAT SOLUBLE VITAMINS

These vitamins require the presence of fat or oil in order to be properly absorbed and digested. They are then stored in body tissues. Some are absorbed better if the food is cooked.

VITAMIN A

This vitamin is essential for vision, growth, the immune system and more. The active form of vitamin A is found in animal products, but it can be synthesized in your body from carotenoids such as beta-carotene. This substance is found in many plant foods, especially orange-yellow plants and leafy greens. Beta-carotene is also a potent antioxidant, unlike animal-derived vitamin A. Foods rich in vitamin A include red bell peppers, carrots, pumpkins, kale and many more.

VITAMIN E

This vitamin acts as an antioxidant and is most known for protecting polyunsaturated fatty acids (PUFA) from free radicals, which are associated with disease. Vitamin E is found mostly in nuts and seeds. Foods rich in vitamin E include almonds, peanuts, avocado, hazelnuts, and sunflower oil.

VITAMIN K

Vitamin K is crucial for the regulation of blood clotting, therefore people who take anticoagulant medications should carefully monitor the amount of vitamin K present in their diet. The main source of vitamin K is plants, especially leafy vegetables, soybeans and some oils. Additionally, a small amount of vitamin K is synthesized by bacteria in our gut. Foods rich in vitamin K include kale, broccoli, collard greens, spinach and cabbage.

VITAMIN B12

PLAYS A ROLE IN BLOOD-CELL FORMATION AND PROPER NERVOUS SYSTEM FUNCTION.

A DEFICIENCY MAY LEAD TO:

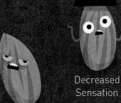

Weakness

Decreased Sensation

Memory Loss

Anemia

Irreversible Nerve Damage

High Levels of Homocysteine, which is associated with Risk of Heart Disease

This vitamin is synthesized by creatures like bacteria, fungi and algae.

In developed countries, before food is marketed, it typically loses almost all of its B12 content when cleaned of contaminants. This includes B12-producing bacteria. Still, it is recommended we wash our food to avoid illness.

Plant foods may have some B12 if contaminated by B12-producing bacteria. Animals might get this vitamin by eating these plants or by absorbing B12 made by their intestinal bacteria.

The human intestines are also home to B12-producing bacteria, but we aren't sure how much gets absorbed. Most of the production occurs so far into the colon that it ends up in feces.

Some foods contain vitamin B12 analogs. This inactive form of the vitamin may interfere with active vitamin B12.

Some foods, like fermented vegetables and algae (such as spirulina), may contain B12 in unknown amounts, which means they are not a reliable source for this vitamin.

How can you make sure you are getting enough B12? Fortified foods are one option, when eaten in satisfying amounts on a regular basis. B12 supplements offer a simple alternative. With either solution, routine blood tests should be taken to confirm healthy levels of B12.

VITAMIN D

Vitamin D plays a meaningful role in calcium regulation, making it important for bone health. With sufficient exposure to sunlight, our bodies can synthesize vitamin D in healthy amounts.

Our modern lifestyle combined with our awareness of sun damage has led us to lower our exposure to the sun. As a result, we get less of this important vitamin.

It is estimated we can meet our vitamin D needs by exposing our hands and face to sunlight for 10-15 minutes at least 2-3 times per week during the summer.

Dark-skinned and older individuals require significantly longer exposure. If you lack sun exposure, you'll need to add vitamin D through enriched foods or supplements (make sure they're vegan!).

MINERALS

IODINE

Crucial for healthy thyroid function. Your thyroid is in charge of metabolism and other functions involving the heart, brain, muscles and more. Some foods contain goitrogens, which interfere with iodine absorption. Goitrogenic foods include soy products and cruciferous vegetables like cabbage, broccoli and cauliflower. The good news: goitrogens are no concern for individuals with normal thyroid function and adequate iodine intake.

Good sources of iodine include seaweed, iodized salt, iodine-fortified foods like fortified breads, and – in some parts of the world – tap water.

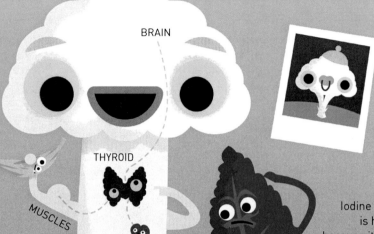

BRAIN

THYROID

MUSCLES

HEART

Iodine is essential for growth during fetal and childhood development.

Iodine content in foods is hard to measure because it depends on the soil where the food grew. Estimates may vary greatly due to insufficient data.

Please note: Iodine content of seaweed varies greatly, so its consumption could cause you to take in excessive amounts. Read the label to determine how much to eat.

ZINC

Necessary for multiple enzyme function, wound healing, growth, immune system operation, maintenance of the sense of taste, and more.

Good sources of zinc: quinoa, beans, peanuts & peanut butter, wheat germ, cashews and other nuts.

It's better to eat zinc-rich foods throughout the day rather than all in one meal.

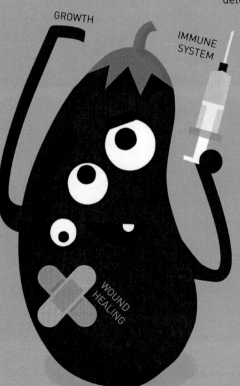

GROWTH

IMMUNE SYSTEM

WOUND HEALING

The Recommended Dietary Allowance (RDA) of zinc intake is not different for vegans, but it's generally recommended for vegans to consume more than omnivores.

Although vegan zinc intake is similar to or slightly lower than omnivore intake, absorption of zinc is lower due to inhibitors in plant foods. The good news: There are many ways to reduce phytate content (like soaking and cooking).

SELENIUM

Necessary for proper functioning of Glutathione – a potent antioxidant. Also needed for thyroid function. Selenium content in food varies based on the mineral content of the soil in which it was grown. This means it's possible for the same food to have different selenium amounts, if it was grown in different areas. Brazil nuts are the best source for selenium. Beans, cereals and grains are also important sources.

 # MAGNESIUM

Required for the function of more than 300 enzymes, making it the most popular nutrient in the human body. Known mainly for its role in bone health. For good sources of magnesium, look to nuts, seeds, grains, beans, seaweed and some vegetables.

 # PHOSPHORUS

Highly involved in bone development. Also important for energy production. It can be found in most plant foods.

 # POTASSIUM

The main mineral inside the cells of your body. Important for muscle contraction, blood pressure, nerve function and bone health. Achieving potassium intake-goals is easy. Plant foods are excellent sources, especially vegetables, beans and fruits.

OMEGA-3 & OMEGA-6

These are two families of unsaturated fatty acids which the human body is unable to create on its own. That means it is essential to get these substances from foods. The most well-known are omega-6 LA (linoleic acid) and omega-3 ALA (alpha linoleic acid), which are necessary for skin health, reproduction and cholesterol metabolism. They may also play a part in decreasing the risk for cardiovascular disease.

When ALA are consumed, the body converts small amounts to different fatty acids, called EPA and DHA. These are important for brain development and eye function. They also protect against cardiac risks and may offer protection from Alzheimer's disease, depression and osteoporosis.

Because LA and ALA use similar pathways in the body, consuming much larger amounts of LA in relation to ALA may limit the synthesis of EPA. This makes it important to include sources of omega-3 in your diet, especially if you are pregnant or lactating.

CHIA SEEDS

WALNUTS

FLAXSEED (GROUND)

HEMPSEED OIL

FREE TO GO!

Ω3

SUPPLEMENTS

CANOLA OIL

FLAXSEED OIL

The best sources of omega-3 are chia seeds, ground flaxseed, flaxseed oil, and canola oil. Additional sources include hemp seed oil, walnuts, and, to a lesser extent, soybeans and leafy green vegetables. It is also possible to get these fatty acids from algae-derived supplements.

Omega-6 is much more abundant and can be found in almost every oil, seed, and nut. High-LA oils such as safflower, sunflower, cottonseed, corn and soybean oils are usually found in processed foods, so limiting your intake of processed products will help lower your LA consumption to achieve a healthy balance.

RECOMMENDED DIETARY ALLOWANCE (RDA)

RDA is the average daily intake of a specific vitamin or mineral that is needed to meet the nutrient requirements for most healthy people. It is expressed in a number of mg/mcg that are needed daily and varies based on age, sex and physical condition.

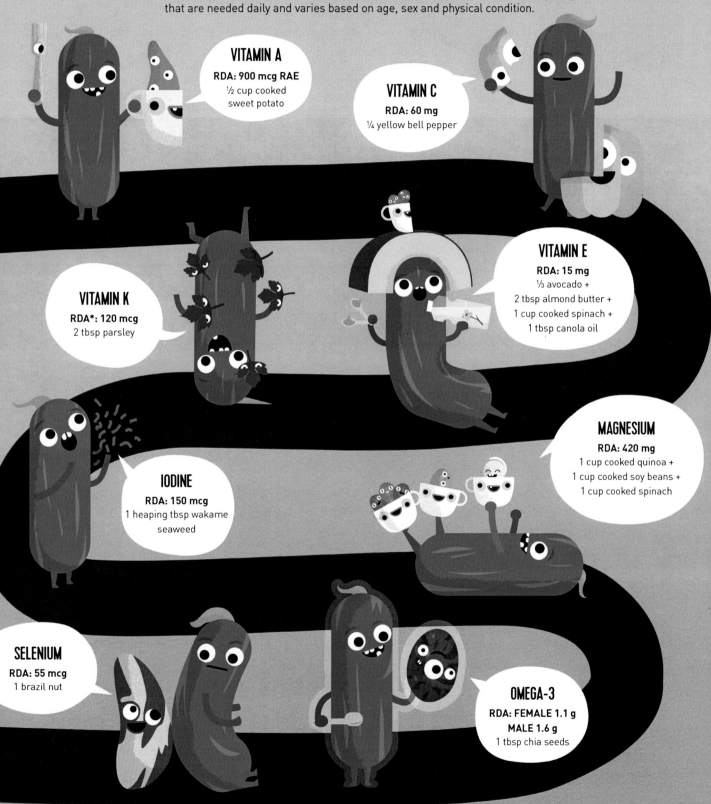

VITAMIN A
RDA: 900 mcg RAE
½ cup cooked sweet potato

VITAMIN C
RDA: 60 mg
¼ yellow bell pepper

VITAMIN E
RDA: 15 mg
⅓ avocado +
2 tbsp almond butter +
1 cup cooked spinach +
1 tbsp canola oil

VITAMIN K
RDA*: 120 mcg
2 tbsp parsley

MAGNESIUM
RDA: 420 mg
1 cup cooked quinoa +
1 cup cooked soy beans +
1 cup cooked spinach

IODINE
RDA: 150 mcg
1 heaping tbsp wakame seaweed

SELENIUM
RDA: 55 mcg
1 brazil nut

OMEGA-3
RDA: FEMALE 1.1 g
MALE 1.6 g
1 tbsp chia seeds

Please note: These are merely suggestions. You can reach all RDAs by following a varied plant-based meal plan.

* Vitamin K doesn't have an RDA value. Instead, it is measured in AI units (adequate intake).

MEET FIBER

Adults should consume 14 g of fiber per 1,000 calories, or 25 g for women and 38 g for men per day. However, only 5% of the population meets this standard. On average, Americans only consume 17 g/day.

Because they are indigestible, fibers fill your stomach without adding calories.

Dietary fiber is defined as nondigestible carbohydrates found only in plants. It offers multiple benefits for the body.

Some fiber reduces LDL ("bad") cholesterol.

Fiber can't be broken down and absorbed by your digestive system but that's why it holds many benefits to your body.

Fermentable fibers are degraded by the good bacteria that populate your gut to yield gases and short-chain fatty acids (SCFAs,) which enhance the health of colon cells.

SCFAs lower the pH in the colon, increasing the bioavailability of some minerals and inhibiting the growth of pathogenic bacteria.

Increasing fiber intake reduces the risk of several chronic conditions, including cardiovascular disease, type 2 diabetes and some cancers. It has also been associated with lower body weight.

Dietary fiber increases fecal bulk, which increases stool frequency and decreases transit time. This reduces the colon's exposure to cancerous compounds found in your feces.

KNOW YOUR DIETARY FIBER

COOKED LENTILS
8 g / ½ cup

COOKED BLACK BEANS
7.5 g / ½ cup

COOKED LIMA BEANS
6.5 g / ½ cup

COOKED BROCCOLI
5.5 g / 1 cup

PASSION FRUIT
5.5 g / 3 units

COOKED SWEET POTATO
4 g / 1 unit

COOKED EDAMAME
4 g / ½ cup

BRUSSELS SPROUTS
4 g / 1 cup

COOKED BULGUR
4 g / ½ cup

APPLE
3.5 g / 1 unit

BANANA
2.5 g / 1 unit

RED BELL PEPPER
2.5 g / 1 unit

COOKED QUINOA
2.5 g / ½ cup

OATS
2 g / 3 tbsp

WHOLE WHEAT BREAD
1.5 g / 1 slice

CARROT
1 g / 1 unit

TIPS TO PRESERVE NUTRIENTS

COOKED TOMATOES PROVIDE MORE LYCOPENE

Cooking tomatoes breaks down plant cells to release more lycopene... but it may also reduce the vitamin content. Mix cooked and raw to get the highest nutritional value.

SOAK AND SPROUT

This process removes much of the phytic acid and other anti-nutrients and unlocks protein and minerals so our bodies can more easily absorb them. Sprouting also increases vitamin content, and it makes food easier to digest.

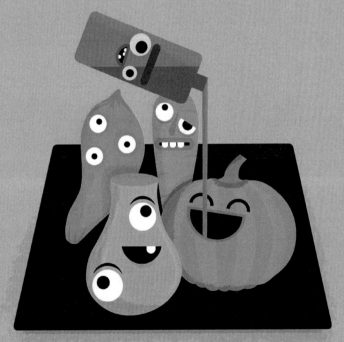

CAROTENOIDS

Carotenoids provide vitamin A and are a strong antioxidant. The darker the veggie, the greater the carotenoid content. To enhance carotenoid absorption, cook vegetables and add a little oil.

DO NOT PEEL VEGETABLES AND FRUITS

The peel contains vitamins, minerals, and a significant amount of dietary fiber. Wash fruits and vegetables thoroughly and eat them whole.

STEAM VEGETABLES INSTEAD OF BOILING

Steaming is one of the best ways to preserve nutrients, water soluble vitamins, and minerals. Since the vegetables don't come in contact with cooking water during steaming, they lose fewer vitamins and minerals!

CHAPTER 6:
FAMILY

Congrats on the new babies, Miss Tomato!
I'm sure they'll be as tasty and red as their mom!

I'd like to show you how a plant-based diet can support
a healthy lifestyle at every age.

I'M EXPECTING...

RAISING VEGAN CHILDREN

Exclusive breastfeeding is recommended for the first 6 months.

If you prefer to use a commercial infant formula, there are a variety of soy-based options available.

Complementary foods should be rich in energy, protein, iron, and zinc. These may include: Lentils, tofu, well-cooked beans and mashed avocado.

Parents can give children fortified soy milk as early as one year of age if the toddler is growing normally and eating a variety of foods.

Vegan children and teens are less likely to be overweight or obese than their non-vegan peers. Children and adolescents with BMI values in the normal range are more likely to stay in the normal range as adults. This significantly reduces risk of disease.

Additional benefits of a plant-based diet during childhood and adolescence include greater consumption of fruits and vegetables, reduced consumption of sweets and salty snacks, and lower intakes of saturated fat. By consuming a balanced vegan diet early in life, children can establish healthy lifelong habits.

To plan nutritionally adequate diets for young vegans, give special attention to these nutrients: iron, zinc, vitamin B12, calcium and vitamin D.

On average, vegan children generally meet or exceed recommended protein intakes. The protein needs of vegan children may be slightly higher than those of non-vegan children because of differences in protein digestibility and amino acid composition.

Consult a dietitian to ensure you provide your children all necessary nutrients.

PREGNANCY & LACTATION

It is well known that maternal diet and lifestyle choices influence the long-term health of both mother and child. It is always essential to eat a varied, nutrient-rich plant-based diet, but doing so while pregnant and lactating is even more important.

Research indicates that vegan pregnancy outcomes, such as birth weight and pregnancy duration, are similar to those of non-vegan pregnancies. Maternal diets high in plant foods may reduce the risk of pregnancy complications, such as gestational diabetes, and may reduce the risk of excessive gestational weight.

The key points: Stay active and eat a varied, nutrient-rich diet that includes the right supplements.

Nutritional factors to be considered: Starting with the second trimester, you need to increase calorie and protein intake in order to support normal fetus and maternal tissue growth. Don't worry, this increase should be about 25 g of protein and around 300 calories, which will probably happen naturally with your increased appetite.

Several nutrients are essential immediately prior to, during, and right after pregnancy. Some you should get through increased food consumption:

ZINC

CALCIUM

IODINE

ALA (OMEGA-3)

Other recommended nutrients you should get through supplements: **FOLIC ACID, IRON, VITAMIN D, DHA (OMEGA-3).**

VITAMIN B12 Pregnant and lactating vegans need regular, adequate supplemental sources of this vitamin, because the mother's stored B12 is not available to the fetus, and the fetus needs freshly absorbed B12. For this reason, it's best for vegans to take a B12 supplement daily.

There are many factors to consider during pregnancy and lactation, including the various dietary supplements that health organizations recommend. It's best to customize your eating plan and supplements to your individual needs, so consult a dietitian to create a personalized healthy eating plan for this period.

Unless otherwise advised by a doctor, it is recommended that you engage in moderate physical activity during pregnancy. This benefits your overall health and may reduce excessive weight gain during and after pregnancy.

TIPS FOR A HEALTHY AND SAFE PREGNANCY

To increase your protein and calorie intake, eat more legumes that provide high-quality protein, as well as more nuts and seeds, which are rich in healthy oils and essential minerals.

If you find it difficult to eat more due to feelings of nausea or heaviness, try eating small, frequent meals. Shakes made of fruits, nuts and soy milk are also good.

Try these foods to help with nausea: Toast, crackers, unroasted almonds, tea with ginger root.

To help avoid foodborne illness during pregnancy, don't eat uncooked sprouted foods. Additionally, when eating in restaurants, only choose establishments where surroundings are clean and food is fresh.

Avoid energy drinks and alcohol and limit coffee to 1-2 cups a day.

Some herbs are forbidden during pregnancy. Consult your healthcare provider before consuming herbal capsules or any teas made from medicinal plants.

MAKING FOOD FUN!

How can you get kids to love their veggies? Make food fun! Here are some ideas to try with your kids. Kids love games and make-believe. If you make food preparation a game, they'll love it!

TOMATO SLICES

ASPARAGUS

LETTUCE

MISS TOMATO

OLIVE

KOHLRABI SLICES

SLICED MUSHROOM LEG

HALF BEETROOT SLICE

SMALL RADISH SLICES

CUCUMBER AIRLINES

SLICED CARROT

GREEN BELL PEPPER

HALF SLICED CUCUMBER

CAULIFLOWER

OLIVE

GREEN
BEAN

AVOCADO
SLICE

HAPPY WORM

BRUSSELS
SPROUTS

HALF
SLICED CHERRY
TOMATO

ORANGE
SLICES

BLUEBERRIES

GRAPE

FOREST

BROCCOLI

SLICED
BANANA

ALL KINDS OF
GREEN LEAVES

KITTY

HALF
STRAWBERRY

MASHED
AVOCADO

CORN

101

EASY SANDWICH SPREADS

A plant-based diet brings you to an entirely new sandwich buffet! Delicious spreads offer tasty flavors and rich nutrition that do way more than simply moisten the bread.

SPINACH

Rich in magnesium, potassium, vitamin K and beta-carotene

| 1 (16 oz) package frozen chopped spinach, thawed and squeeze dried | ½ cup shredded carrots | 1 (12 oz) container vegan cream cheese | 1 (8 oz) can water chestnuts, chopped | 1 tbsp dried minced onion | ½ tsp garlic granules | 2 green onions, chopped |

Combine all ingredients in a bowl and chill for two hours.

AVOCADO

Rich in calcium, potassium and healthy fat

| 1 smashed avocado | 3 tbsp fresh lemon juice | 4 small radish, shredded | 1 green onion, chopped | Salt and black pepper to taste | 150 g smashed tofu |

Combine all ingredients in a bowl. Enjoy.

TAHINI

Rich in calcium and iron

| ½ cup raw whole tahini | ¼ cup cold water | ¼ cup lemon juice | A pinch of salt | 1 garlic clove, minced |

Combine all ingredients in a bowl. Start spreading!

BABA GHANOUSH

Rich in antioxidants

| Poke 2 eggplants with a fork several times. Bake at 460°F (240°C) for around 40 minutes. Allow eggplants to cool, then slice open and scoop out the flesh. | 2 tbsp raw whole tahini | Salt and black pepper to taste | 1 garlic clove, minced |

Place ingredients in a bowl and mix with strong, quick strokes until eggplant forms a rough paste.

WALNUT

Rich in omega-3 fatty acids

| 1 cup walnuts | ¼ cup water | 2 tbsp lemon juice | A pinch of salt, ¼ tbsp black pepper | 1 garlic clove, minced | 3 tbsp chopped sun-dried tomatoes |

Combine all ingredients in a food processor, process until smooth.

CHOCOLATE

Rich in vitamin E and antioxidants

| 1 cup raw hazelnuts | ⅓ cup pure maple syrup | ¼ cup cacao powder | ¼ cup water | 2 tbsp coconut oil | 1 tbsp vanilla extract | Pinch of salt |

Place ingredients in a blender and mix on high for approximately one minute (until texture is creamy and smooth).

GROW THESE FOODS — FROM KITCHEN SCRAPS!

LETTUCE

Place the base in a container of water in a warm, sunny location. After a few days, roots will form. You can then transplant your mini lettuce into soil. To harvest, simply cut the lettuce, leaving about 2 inches of growth, and let the plant grow again.

CELERY

Set the celery base in water and leave it until roots begin to form, then transplant it to soil. Let the plant grow until it is large enough to harvest – usually about 8 inches.

GARLIC

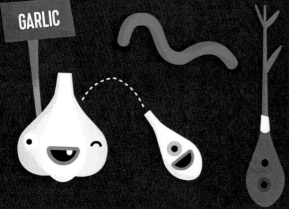

Plant a garlic clove in a sunny spot of soil, root-end down. Trim off shoots as they appear, to encourage bulb growth. Harvest and repeat the process for a never-ending cycle of fresh garlic!

ONION

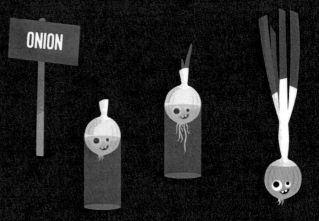

Place root base in water until roots start to form, then transplant into potting soil. As it grows, you can trim the onion greens for green onions or let a new bulb form.

GINGER

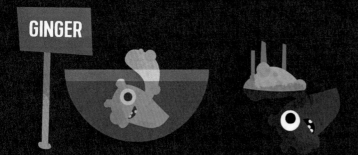

Soak until ginger bud swells, then plant - keeping half the root above the surface. Roots will soon sprout and grow fresh ginger!

POTATO

Cut off the eye of a sprouting potato. (Include a bit of flesh.) Plant the piece in potting soil. With faithful watering, you'll soon have a new potato plant!

SWEET POTATO

Place the root in water, arranging it so at least one sprout is near the top, above the water line. Transfer it to a pot once it starts to grow (or the ground if you are in a warm enough climate).

BASIL

Place a cutting of basil in water until roots begin to form, then transplant to soil.

CARROT GREENS

Carrots and other root vegetables can all be grown again using their tops. Put the carrot tops in a dish with a little water. When they start sprouting, put them in potting soil and keep them slightly damp and warm. The tops will root and eventually sprout new vegetables beneath the surface. Use this same method to regrow other root veggies!

PUMPKIN

Rinse and dry pumpkin seeds, then plant. Use warm, rich soil. Pumpkins don't like cold weather, so be sure Jack Frost is gone for the season before you plant them outside.

TOMATO

Slice a tomato into ¼-inch-thick pieces. Place these into a compost pot and add compost and/or potting soil until slices are barely covered. Water every other day. In less than two weeks, you should have up to five dozen seedlings.

BELL PEPPER

Simply remove the seeds from the parent pepper and plant!

CHAPTER 7

EXERCISE
& WEIGHT

A plant-based diet can provide all the nutrients you need for an active lifestyle. The goal of your activity will influence your food choices! Let's work out!

MAINTAINING YOUR WEIGHT

Increase vegetable consumption. Raw, boiled, cooked, or steamed – any which way is good! Veggies are high in fiber and water, which means they make you feel full on fewer calories.

Change the proportions on your plate. Make more room for vegetables and less room for rice and potatoes. A good proportion for a meal is ½ vegetables, ¼ beans and ¼ grains.

Always keep a healthy snack in your drawer at work or in a bag when away from home.

Eat slowly and concentrate on your eating. It takes some time for fullness signals to appear, so eating quickly or when busy doing something else usually results in eating more than you need.

Be as active as you can. Take the stairs instead of the elevator; don't park in the closest spot to your office; etc. – and, of course, exercise!

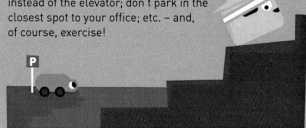

Try swapping one of your meals for a salad. Do this every day or once a week – you decide. Just don't forget to include beans!

Don't wait until you're really hungry to eat. This makes it harder to choose wisely, eat slowly and avoid overeating. On the other hand, don't eat if you're not hungry, just because it's meal time.

Almonds, walnuts, chia and other nuts and seeds are super healthy, but they contain a lot of fat. This means they're high in calories, too, so limit your consumption of these foods to a handful a day. Try to stick to natural and unsalted or fried varieties.

Drink lots of water! In addition to other benefits of hydration, water fills the stomach and helps you feel less hungry.

Cut down on junk food and processed foods. They usually contain a lot more fat, sugar, salt and additives than home-made foods.

1 Try adding shakes made of fruits, nuts and seeds to your diet.

2 Use high-calorie spreads for sandwiches: tahini, natural peanut butter, avocado, etc.

3 Eat many small meals. This will help you increase your caloric consumption.

4 Don't base your diet on junk food. Although high in calories, it's also really bad for your health.

GUIDE FOR THE *PHYSICALLY ACTIVE*

Physical activity can lower the risk of cardiovascular disease and a wide range of other chronic illnesses, including type 2 diabetes, colon and breast cancer, obesity, hypertension, depression and bone and joint disease.

People who participate in a general fitness program (e.g. exercising 30-40 min/day, 3 times a week) can typically meet nutritional needs following a normal diet because their caloric demands from exercise are not too great. This means it is not necessary to load up on protein or other nutrients.

People who participate in a more strict training program would benefit from consulting a sports dietitian. This professional can help create a menu that suits their needs based on activity level.

CUCUMBER PLANK

CARROT PUSH-UP

BEETROOT LUNGE

PUSH-UP AND ROTATION ALMOND

APPLE WALL SIT

LEMON SQUAT

JUMPING AVOCADO

ABDOMINAL CRUNCH KALE

HIGH PERSIMMON KNEES RUNNING IN PLACE

A typical, physically active person can find all the nutrients they need in a balanced, varied, plant-based diet that includes B12 supplementation.

Vegans generally have a higher antioxidant consumption than omnivores, specifically vitamin C, vitamin E and beta-carotene. This may help reduce exercise-induced oxidative stress.

TIPS FOR THE *PHYSICALLY ACTIVE*

Eat 3 large meals and healthy snacks between meals.

Spread mineral- and protein-rich foods, like legumes, seeds, and nuts, throughout your day rather than pack all of them in one meal.

Drink lots of water.

Avoid eating a large meal for at least 2 hours before exercise to stay light and limber for your workout.

Fuel up on antioxidants by eating all colors of fruits and vegetables.

Eat fruit 30 minutes before exercise for an energy boost.

After working out, eat a well-balanced meal consisting of quality protein, complex carbohydrates and lots of vegetables. (Pre-workout meals should be the same.)

THE VEGAN vs. NON-VEGAN OLYMPIC GAMES

*All legumes and meat are cooked

WINNER!

LENTILS
3.3 mg iron/100 g

IRON SHOT PUT

CHICKEN BREAST
1.5 mg iron/100 g

CALCIUM-IRON FENCING

WINNER!

WHOLE SEED TAHINI
120 mg calcium/tbsp
1 mg iron/tbsp

EGG MAYO
1 mg calcium/tbsp
0 mg iron/tbsp

PROTEIN FIGURE SKATING

WINNER!

COOKED EDAMAME
12 g protein/100 g

COTTAGE CHEESE
11 g protein/100 g

IRON POLE VAULT

WINNER!

CHICKPEAS
3 mg iron/100 g

PORK
1 mg iron/100 g

CALCIUM-IRON WEIGHTLIFTING

GROUND BEEF
9 mg calcium/100 g
3 mg iron/100 g

WINNER!

WHITE BEANS
90 mg calcium/100 g
3.5 mg iron/100 g

PROTEIN-IRON SYNCHRONISED SWIMMING

WINNER!

TOFU
15 g protein/100 g
2.5 mg iron/100 g

EGGS
12.5 g protein/2 eggs
1 mg iron/2 eggs

CHAPTER 8

ANIMALS
& THE ENVIRONMENT

Animals are beautiful, cute, sentient creatures. Raising them for food requires massive amounts of land, food, energy, and water, and, of course, it causes immense suffering.

51% or more of the global greenhouse-gas emissions are caused by animal agriculture!

Allow me to show you some facts.

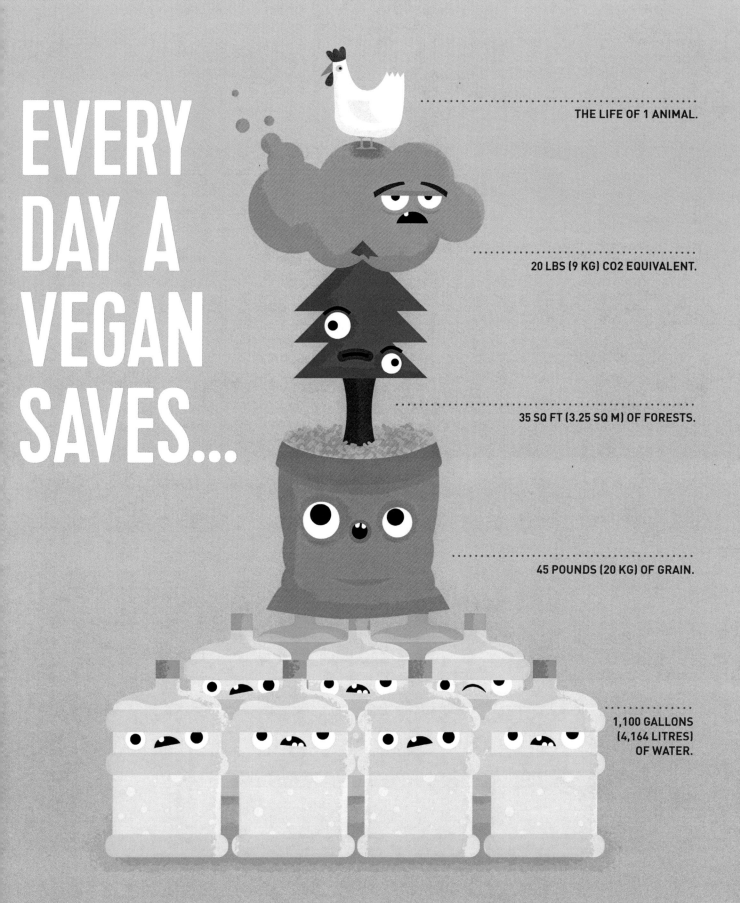

EVERY DAY A VEGAN SAVES...

THE LIFE OF 1 ANIMAL.

20 LBS (9 KG) CO2 EQUIVALENT.

35 SQ FT (3.25 SQ M) OF FORESTS.

45 POUNDS (20 KG) OF GRAIN.

1,100 GALLONS
(4,164 LITRES)
OF WATER.

WE CAN ALL MAKE A DIFFERENCE. EVERY CHOICE WE MAKE MATTERS.
IF ENOUGH PEOPLE MAKE THE BEST CHOICES, WE CAN IMPACT OUR PLANET.

IN 1 YEAR, THE AVG. AMERICAN CONSUMES...

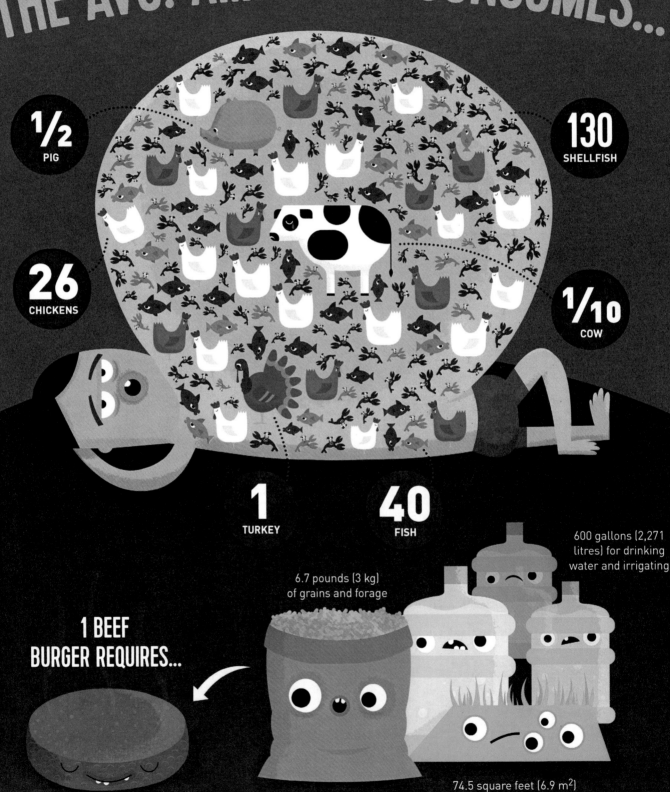

½ PIG

26 CHICKENS

130 SHELLFISH

¹/₁₀ COW

1 TURKEY

40 FISH

1 BEEF BURGER REQUIRES...

6.7 pounds (3 kg) of grains and forage

600 gallons (2,271 litres) for drinking water and irrigating

74.5 square feet (6.9 m²) for grazing and growing feed crops

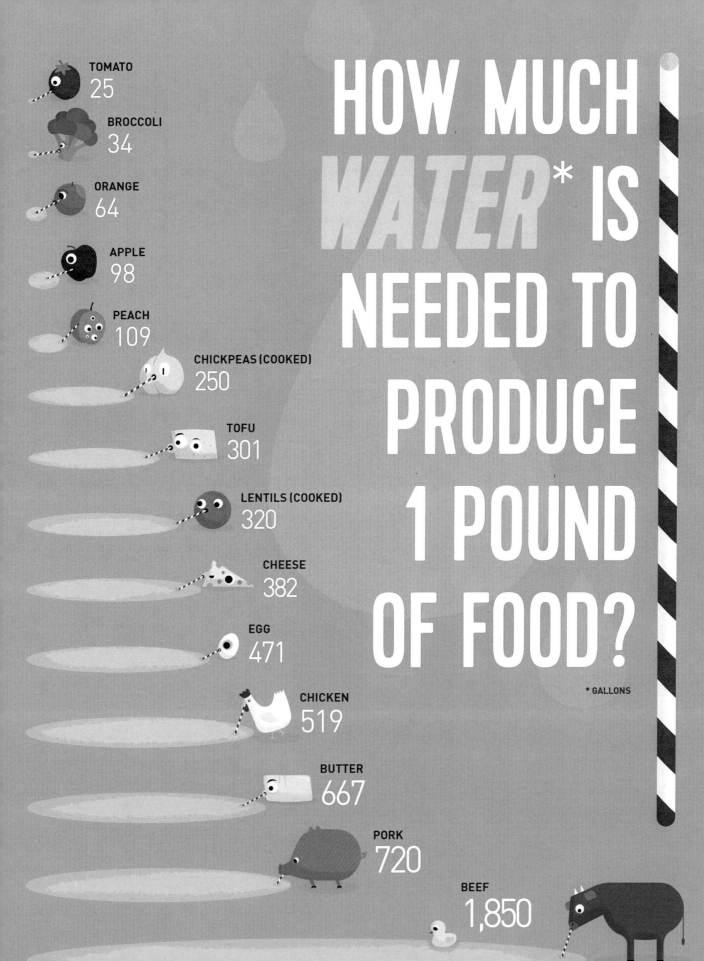

HOW MUCH *WATER** IS NEEDED TO PRODUCE 1 POUND OF FOOD?

* GALLONS

TOMATO
25

BROCCOLI
34

ORANGE
64

APPLE
98

PEACH
109

CHICKPEAS (COOKED)
250

TOFU
301

LENTILS (COOKED)
320

CHEESE
382

EGG
471

CHICKEN
519

BUTTER
667

PORK
720

BEEF
1,850

SURPRISING ANIMAL FACTS

Pigs dream.

Pigs are the 4th most intelligent animal on earth. They are smarter than dogs and 3-year-olds.

Cows have panoramic vision. They can see more than 300 degrees at a time. (Pretty impressive compared to our 140-degree vision!)

Pigs don't sweat, so they take mud baths to cool off.

Cows can hear sounds at lower volumes and higher frequencies than humans can.

Pigs are extremely social animals. They form close bonds with others. They love contact and enjoy getting massages.

Hi!

Have you heard the phrase "pecking order?" This comes from the complex social structures chickens create. Each animal knows his or her place - and who's boss!

Chickens love to sunbathe – wings outstretched, eyes closed.

Mother hens talk to their chicks while they are still in the egg.

Hens defend their young from predators.

Chickens have full-color vision.

When separated from their families, cows grieve. They even shed tears over their loss.

Sheep visibly express their emotions.

Sheep are extremely intelligent animals, capable of problem solving. They are considered to have an IQ similar to that of cows, and they are nearly as clever as pigs.

Cows enjoy the intellectual challenge of solving problems and get excited when they find a solution.

Sheep are strong swimmers. In search of better pastures, they will even cross rivers and lakes!

When sheep are sick, they can detect what nutrients they need and seek out plants that make them feel better. They can test foods to learn which ones are beneficial or toxic.

Female sheep are very caring mothers. When their lambs wander too far away, they can recognize them by their call.

Fish are able to navigate dark or murky waters due to a unique sense organ that functions like personal radar.

Fish use their mouths to gather rocks, collect food and create nests for their young.

Fish have been around a while. Scientists trace back their ancestry on Earth more than 450 million years.

Some fish make sounds by grating their teeth.

Like birds and mammals, fish feel pain and suffer.

HOW AMAZING PIGS ARE! MEET...
ESTHER THE WONDER PIG!

Steven Jenkins and his life partner Derek Walter were living an ordinary life when a would-be-rescued mini pig came into their lives. Esther quickly stole their hearts and turned their lives upside down. In just two short years, Esther amassed hundreds of thousands of followers from all over the world. In 2014, with their help, Happily Ever Esther Farm Sanctuary was born. Now, Esther and her dads rescue and rehabilitate abandoned and abused farm animals and spread Esther's style of love and compassion - known as The Esther Effect! This world-changing star granted Simple Happy Kitchen an exclusive interview.

Hey Esther! You're a rockstar. Any thoughts on what it is about your story that caught people's attention?

That would be my smile! And the fact that I was living inside a house with my own mattress and couch. I mean, how many 650-pound pigs do you know that live inside of a house just like their humans?

How many animals live in the sanctuary today?

There are over 50 animals, and they're all my friends. Especially Captain Dan - I have a big ole crush on him.

Do all animals in the sanctuary get along? Or are there different groups who live in different areas?

Everyone has their own herd. The chickens roam together; pig April and her 5 children are a herd; pigs Captain Dan, Leonard, and Bobbie are a pack; Bj the donkey and Escalade the horse are inseparable friends, and they reside in our biggest pasture with our cows Pouty Face, Jasmine, and Sir Denver. We also have a bunny town area for the rabbits and a goat and sheep field. It's hard not to get along when you know nothing but kindness and love from our dads. It makes us give it back tenfold to each other.

Who is your favorite famous animal? Are there any fellow pigs (or cats) you especially like?

Well there isn't any one animal, but I do follow many other sanctuary pages. I like to see how my kind lives, and I often spend many hours watching videos and looking at pictures. My best friend is my dog sister Shelby. She became my surrogate mom the day Dad Steve brought me home, and she's always by my side. She even licks my snout after meals to clean away any crumbs.

What does your day look like?

My day starts off at a leisurely pace - I am NOT a morning pig, and I've been known to sleep till noon some days. A diva needs her beauty rest. Once I'm up, I saunter down to the dining room, or as the volunteers refer to it, 'The Barn' and the other residents refer to as 'Home.' After eating a low-fat, specially-milled kibble breakfast, I stroll through the barn saying good morning to everyone. Sometimes, if I'm exhausted after all the greetings, I will find an empty stall and have a nap in the straw for an hour or so. It's important to stay close to my roots and see how the other half lives. After my nap, my dads usually take me on a perimeter walk of our property. There are 49 acres, and on that excursion I say hello to all of our other animals. Everybody is always excited to see my dads, but secretly I think it's because they know it is MY Sanctuary, and they have to pay their respect. The rest of my day I spend supervising my dads, or I sleep. I love to sleep.

Is there anything you don't like to eat?

Kale! I despise kale. I much prefer **cupcakes**! Cupcakes get such a bad rap, when they are really muffins who have achieved their dreams. My favorites are peanut butter or strawberry frosted. People think that all I eat are cupcakes, but there is a big difference between my 'Facebook' diet and my real-life diet.

Where do you see yourself a year from now?

I would like to try my hoof at cooking. Fans know my dads are not the best cooks, so if I can whip up some easy recipes for them to try, I think I might try and write a cookbook.

Other than your amazing presence on social media, are you active elsewhere? How do you spread the word about your ideology?

Yes, I'm active via my dad's books! They wrote a New York Times bestseller, "Esther the Wonder Pig: Changing the World One Heart at a Time," and a children's book that will reach a whole new audience. And, the sequel to dads' first book!

BUYING CRUELTY-FREE CLOTHES

Cruelty-free clothing is available at nearly every retail store. To find these items,
you simply need to identify vegan and non-vegan products and materials on the labels.
Pay close attention, because animal products can hide in unexpected places.

LEATHER

Don't buy: leather, suede, sheepskin, angora, shearling, nubuck. Look for these symbols to make sure you're not buying leather:

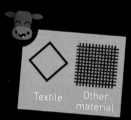

Leather Coated leather Textile Other material

FUR

You probably won't see the word "fur" on the label. To make sure you aren't buying any animal fur, choose clothing with labels that indicate faux fur, polyester, acrylic, or modacrylic.

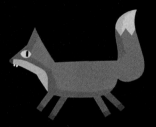

SILK

Look carefully for this one. Often, this material makes up less than a fifth of the product, so its listing can get hidden in the label among other materials.

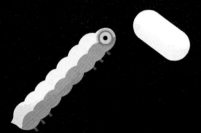

WOOL

Watch for wool blends that may hide this material's presence. You can also identify wool products by the name of their animal source: alpaca, angora, cashmere, chiengora, llama, lopi, merino, mohair, Tibetan fur, or vicugna.

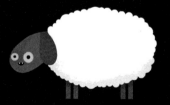

DOWN

This is the soft layer of feathers closest to birds' skin. Make sure these don't appear on the label: crushed feathers, plumage, landfowl plumage, waterfowl plumage, down, down blend, down fiber, plumule, feather, feather fiber, feather fillings, residue, commercial down.

CHAPTER 9

NOW IT'S

Thanks for joining me on this adventure! I hope you had a great time.

Now that you and Miss Tomato know everything you need to know about plant-based nutrition from the health, ethical and ecological standpoints, you can try it yourself.

Hope you had a great time learning with me and my friends! To make sure you don't miss anything, I've created a nice checklist just for you on the next page. And remember - a journey of a thousand miles begins with a single almond!

Meanwhile, I'm gonna soak myself for tomorrow's sandwich spread.

See ya!

YOUR TURN!

CHECKLIST FOR GOING VEGAN

☐ **KEEP YOUR MOTIVATION IN MIND**

Once your eyes have been opened to the benefits of a vegan lifestyle, you aren't likely to close them again. Your new understanding of the individual and global effects of animal products changes you and helps you make more changes - and stick to them. Your desire to live a healthy life helps you place your feet on a new path – and never look back.

☐ **SOAK UP KNOWLEDGE**

Boost your confidence with a wealth of knowledge. Learn all you can about your new lifestyle as you make the transition. Books, websites, blogs and other vegans are valuable sources that will provide the insights and support you need.

☐ **START READING LABELS**

Learn about product labels and how to decipher them. Once you become familiar with animal-derived ingredients and how to identify them on product labels, it will become easy to recognize what's vegan and what's not.

☐ **ADD BEFORE YOU SUBTRACT**

It's easier to add foods to your diet than remove them. Make the vegan transition easier by adding more plant-based foods to your diet before you start taking anything out. Try eating more delicious veggies, seeds, nuts, legumes and tofu.

☐ **EXPAND YOUR FOOD REPERTOIRE**

Try new types of foods to prepare to change your lifestyle. Add new vegetables, grains, fruits and legumes to your meals and snacks.

☐ **MAKE YOUR VEGAN MENU APPEALING**

Myriad vegan recipes are available. Find the ones that appeal to your palate. Check out vegan cookbooks or free online recipes. You're certain to discover delicious new dishes as well as new ways to prepare old favorites.

MASTER A FEW SIMPLE, HAPPY MEALS

You might be surprised how many quick and easy vegan meals you can prepare from products already in your kitchen. Learn a few of these to immediately feel like a vegan meal master.

MOOOVE YOUR MILK SELECTION

Switch your dairy milk to almond or soy milk. Many other options are also available. Most people find it easy to discover a non-dairy option they enjoy.

STRENGTHEN YOUR WEAK POINTS

Are you worried about giving up foods you enjoy? Learn about vegan alternatives and new recipe options. This will help you view veganism as a new healthy lifestyle, not a food rut.

GET READY FOR RESISTANCE

No one likes to feel judged. Remember, not too long ago you were eating animal products too.

It's important to keep your end goal in mind and go at your own pace. Some people can switch to a vegan diet overnight. If that's not you, that's ok. Don't worry if you need more time. As with other lifestyle changes, going vegan takes time to adjust. You simply need to determine what works best for you.

Need personal guidance from experienced mentors and registered dietitians? **Challenge 22+** offers a free, supportive online framework! Join over 100,000 people from all over the world, receive tips, recipes and support, 24/7 - for free!

Join at **www.simplehappy.kitchen/challenge22**.

This book was made possible thanks to the amazing support of thousands of people who contributed to my Kickstarter and Indiegogo campaigns. I couldn't have done it without you!

Aaron P. Aaron R. Aaron S. Abigail Abigail T. Adam Adam C. Adam D. Adam S. Adi Adi L. Adi Y. Adrienne G. Agathe L. Aidan A. Aimee C. Aina Aisha B. Aisling G. Al Alaa A. Alan G. Alber R. Albert B. Albert T. Alejandra L. Alejandra P. Aleksandra C. Alena R. Alessandro R. Alex Alex B. Alex D. Alex S. Alexander H. Alexander K. Alexander T. Alexandra C. Alexandra F. Alexandra K. Alexandra R. Alexandra T. Alexandra W. Alexandre L. Alexhaas01 Alfie Algadi Alice B. Alice C. Alice M. Alice S. Alicia Alina G. Alisa Z. Alison Alistair N. Allison H. Allison M. Allison R. Alon R. Alona N. Alyssa C. Alyssa D. Amanda Amanda C. Amanda F. Amanda H. Amanda M. Amanda P. Amanda S. Amane Amber H. Amber W. Amelia W. Amelie Amie R. Amir G. Amirf Amit H. Amit M. Amitay T. Amy Amy C. Amy K. Amy L. Amy R. Amy S. Amy Y. Ana Ana C. Ana S. Ana V. Anat E. Anat K. Andras E. Andrea Andrea A. Andrea F. Andrei L. Andrew H. Andrew K. Andrew L. Andrew M. Andy F. Andy S. Anette T. Angel L. Angela Angela D. Angela I. Angela K. Angela L. Angela O. Angela P. Angelina I. Angharad G. Angie Anjak Ann D. Anna C. Anna K. Annabel C. Annabella C. Annamari R. Annarose Anne Anne F. Anne-Dorthe S. Anne-Marie C. Anne-Marie S. Annejil Annie Annie L. Annie T. Annika S. Anny L. Anny R. Anthony S. Antoine T. Antonette J. Archiesgirl Arelis A. Aresu-Laetitia T. Ari S. Ariela P. Arielle E. Arnon H. Aron M. Art H. Arthur H. Aryadnes P. Asaf B. Ash A. Ashleigh J. Ashley A. Ashley K. Ashley M. Ashley R. Asm Assaf B. Astrid G. Astrid H. Ataraxia S. Audrey T. Aurelie Aurélie B. Aurelien Austin P. Autumn H. Aviv T. Aviya S. Avner G. Avner P. Bar M. Barak D. Barbara B. Barry P. Batel N. Baylacq Bazyli Z. Beatrice Z. Bec E. Becky C. Becky W. Belinda F. Ben C. Ben J. Ben K. Ben S. Benjamin Benjamin D. Benjamin P. Benjamin V. Bernadette G. Bianca Bjoern B. Black G. Blaise A. Blake C. Blaze Bloopidybloop Bobbie-Jo M. Boris Borislav N. Brandi B. Brandon A. Brandon E. Brandon W. Bree G. Brenda W. Brenna F. Brett M. Brian A. Brian N. Briana B. Brianna Y. Brigitte G. Brittany K. Brittany T. Bronte F. Bruno A. Btejeda123 Caitlin C. Caitlin F. Caitlin J. Caleb B. Callista W. Callum M. Cameron H. Cameron T. Camilla L. Candice D. Cara Carin A. Carina V. Carl Carl C. Carmen Carmen B. Carmen K. Carmit R. Carol C. Carole L. Carolin W. Caroline T. Carolyn L. Carolyn S. Casey B. Casey P. Cass Cassandra H. Cassandra K. Cassandra L. Cassie F. Cat Catherine G. Catie W. Cecilie M. Cedric V. Celina L. Chad M. Chan X. Chance Chantal Chantel Chelsea B. Chelsea K. Chen C. Cherise Cheryl D. Cheryl M. Chet B. Chiara Chloe T. Chris B. Chris H. Chris J. Chris L. Chris W. Christian Christian W. Christina Christina D. Christina G. Christina K. Christina N. Christine Christine G. Christine K. Christoffer S. Christopher A. Christopher G. Christopher M. Christopher R. Ciara M. Cid C. Ciena Y. Cilgia B. Cindy E. Cindy H. Cinemajoe Cinthia G. Claire Claire M. Clare M. Clarissa J. Clarity Claude S. Claudia Claudia H. Claudia J. Clay N. Clemens G. Colin D. Concepcion B. Connie W. Connor M. Constanza D. Coral B. Corey E. Corinna W. Courtney A. Craigh Creative M. Cristy H. Crystal P. Curdy M. Cyndee S. D.V. Dafna A. Dag R. Daisy M. Daisy S. Dalila Dalviny T. Damjan C. Dan A. Dan B. Dan C. Dan H. Dan M. Dan T. Dana Dana A. Dana B. Dana F. Dana L. Dana S. Dana W. Dana Y. Danica P. Daniel Akuss Daniel C. Daniel M. Daniel S. Daniel S. Daniel V. Daniela Daniele G. Danielle Danielle W. Danir A. Danni F. Danny B. Dannyel M. Darren S. Das S. Dave G. Dave K. David B. David C. David J. David M. David R. David Z. Davinder M. Dawn J. Dea Dean K. Deb Deb P. Deb W. Deborah Deborah A. Deborah M. Dee C. Delie P. Delvis Denis P. Denise B. Denise S. Dennis K. Denny G. Derek A. Derek J. Derson I. Desiree W. Devin D. Diana Diana M. Dianne Dianne K. Diego P. Din B. Dirkjan L. Dixie T. Djporkscratchings Dominaria Dominic J. Dominic W. Dominik E. Dominika Donald E. Dondi L. Donna D. Donna K. Donna M. Dor B. Dora B. Dorit S. Dorota Dp7 Ebonie Ebrahim A. Eden H. Eduardo A. Eduardo B. Eehad Efrat L. Eileen Eileen H. Eileen S. Eireni F. Ekaterina Elad M. Elad S. Elaine Eldar B. Elder Y. Eleana C. Eleanor W. Elena Elena P. Elfeera Eliane Elina B. Elinore H. Elisa Elisa L. Elisabet B. Elisha C. Eliza P. Elizabeth Elizabeth G. Elizabeth N. Ella Ellen M. Elodie L. Eloise Elvira Emanuela Emilie Emily Emily B. Emily G. Emily H. Emily M. Emily T. Emily W. Emma Emma F. Emma H. Emma S. Emmalee F. Emmanuel R. Envy M. Eran B. Eran S. Erga S. Eric Eric G. Eric M. Eric R. Eric S. Erica Erika Erika B. Erin Erin A. Erin J. Erin K. Erin S. Ester Ester Z. Eszter D. Etai H. Ethan C. Euan Euniece W. Eva Eva J. Eva L. Eva P. Eva S. Evan G. Eve G. Evelien Evelyn Evia Eyal Eyal O. Eynav G. Eytan C. Fabian M. Fabien C. Fabry Fade R. Fanni F. Fanny L. Fanny M. Farren Felecan M. Felipe M. Femke B. Fern B. Fernanda Fernando L. Fernando M. Ferocious V. Filip B. Filip J. Fleur M. Florian E. Foo M. Francine F. François S. Frank H. Frauke P. Freshbiz Friendly N. Gadi B. Gadis Gal Gal A. Gal M. Galadriel Gardner M. Gareth F. Garrett K. Gary G. Gay B. Gearsoul D. Gem G. Gemma Gemma T. Gena Georgimc Georgina Gerard R. Gerasimos K. Gerry C. Gil S. Gilly W. Gina H. Gina M. Girlies A. Giulia L. Glen B. Glenn S. Gloria L. Gm P. Gopinath S. Grace Grace K. Graham J. Greet Greg C. Grzegorz C. Gud N. Guðrún A. Guekoz Guilherme T. Guillermo C. Guillermo G. Guy A. Gwen S. Gwendolyn D. Hadar S. Hadas V. Hagai I. Haimdror Hatelly R. Hamilton S. Han-Chi Y. Hannah Hannah B. Hannah C. Hannah O. Hans G. Harbon-Feferman Haripetrov Heather Heather F. Heather K. Helbrecht Helen P. Helena M. Helena P. Helena S. Helene Henk A. Henk L. Henri A. Henry H. Hestia V. Hila Hila M. Hilary H. Hilla S. Hilla S. Hillary H. Hitomi O. Holl H. Honeybadger Hristo B. Hyun L. Iain P. Idan V. Idit L. Ilan Ilan P. Inbal Inbar E. Iona E. Ipesaj Ir S. Ireen H. Irene C. Irina I. Irit S. Irrational V. Iryna P. Isa B. Isaac B. Isaac W. Isabella Isabella Isabella D. Isabella L. Isabella S. Isis Itai H. Iva J. Ivan L. Ivan P. Ixone P. Jackalgirl Jackii R. Jacob Jacob B. Jacob R. Jacob W. Jacyntha L. Jailyn D. Jaime K. James James A. James B. James C. James T. Jamie H. Jan B. Jan O. Jan S. Jan Š. Janine C. Janne E. Janus S. Jared M. Jasmin Jasmine S. Jason Jason B. Javier R. Jay Y. Jb G. Jeanette V. Jeannette K. Jeff L. Jeff V. Jen G. Jen S. Jenae D. Jenn K. Jennifer Jennifer A. Jennifer C. Jennifer D. Jennifer E. Jennifer F. Jennifer K. Jennifer M. Jennifer S. Jennifer W. Jennine Jenny E. Jenny K. Jenny L. Jerem2174 Jérémy Jeremy J. Jeremy P. Jeremy S. Jesse L. Jesse M. Jessi R. Jessica C. Jessica R. Jessica T. Jessica W. Jessika G. Jiggly P. Jill Jill S. Jillian B. Jillian S. Jim H. Jim L. Jing W. Jo Jo F. Jo K. Jo L. Jo M. Joachim Joan P. Joana M. Jodi Jodi F. Jodie W. Joe B. Joel B. Joep V. Johann P. Johanna F. Johanna M. Johannes P. Johannes S. Johannes W. John H. John K. Johnny Jon M. Jonathan B. Jonathan E. Jonathan N. Joni C. Jonnvoll Jordanne L. Jos S. Jose José D. Jose F. Joseph C. Joseph T. Josh F. Joshua A. Joshua T. Josuŭjo Josue E. Joyce H. Jp K. Juan J. Juan M. Juan P. Juanita M. Judith S. Judy O. Julia Julia B. Julia S. Julia T. Julian E. Julian H. Julian L. Julian M. Julian-Chris R. Juliana S. Julie Julie M. Julie P. Julie R. Julie S. Julie S. Julie T. Julie T. Julien-B. R. Julienne L. Juliette B. Julio L. Julius H. Junto N. Juraj K. Jürgen B. Jürgen R. Justin P. Justin Y. Justine Jye M. Kaelene C. Kahlie Kaisa Kallen L. Kamolpong S. Karen Karen A. Karen F. Karen H. Karen L. Karen T. Karen W. Karenna L. Karin Karin L. Karl M. Karli S. Karolien V. Kat W. Katarzyna P. Kate Kate Kate E. Kate H. Kate O. Kate R. Kate S. Kate-Lyn L. Katharina S. Katherine Katherine F. Kathleen C. Kathleen W. Kathryn G. Kathy S. Kathye A. Katia H. Katie Katie Katie C. Katie W. Katja K. Kayla K. Kayvi H. Kellie E. Kelly Kelly A. Kelly C. Kelly W. Kelman E. Kelsey J. Kelsey K. Ken Ken A. Kenzie Keren R. Kerim P. Kerry A. Kerstin S. Keung C. Kevin Kevin C. Kevin P. Kevin S. Kim Kim L. Kim M. Kim-Sue K. Kimberley B. Kimberly C. Kimberly M. Kinsey F. Kirill L. Kirstie K. Kirstin S. Kollim Kristenvoghelllewis Kristi W. Kristian S. Kristin Kristin A. Kristin S. Kristina C. Kristina S. Krysia F. Krystyna S. Ku H. Kwan Kyle Kyle G. L L B. Laetitia D. Lara B. Lara L. Lara W. Lasar Laura Laura B. Laura D. Laura G. Laura L. Laura P. Lauren H. Lauren L. Lauren P. Laurens K. Laurie Laurie T. Laverne J. Lawrence H. Le R. Lea L. Lea S. Leah E. Leah L. Leah S. Leah V. Leah Z. Ledru A. Lee A. Lee B. Len R. Lena G. Lenneke V. Leon G. Leon M. Leonard G. Leslie Leslie B. Leslie H. Leslie M. Leticia Lewis C. Leynaert B. Libby N. Libby R. Lilith K. Lilly V. Lily Lily V. Lilya Y. Lincoln P. Linda Linda D. Linda R. Lindsay Lindsay D. Lindsay R. Lindsay W. Lior G. Lior P. Liron Lisa Lisa Lisa C. Lisa F. Lisa G. Lisa H. Lisa M. Lisa O. Lisa P. Lisa R. Lisa S. Lisette Lissett D. Lital M. Lital S. Liv Liz Liz L. Liz R. Liz S. Lizzie B. Lizzie G. Lkd Lonneke V. Lordmitz Lorena Lorene S. Lorenzo D. Lori Lou M. Louisa R. Louise Louise S. Lowe Lu K. Lucas R. Lucia Luciana P. Luciano M. Lucy Lucy K. Luis M. Luisa Luiza F. Luka Lupita R. Luree C. Luvgreen Lyndsey K. Lynnette Lythiah Maarten K. Maayan G. Maayan T. Maayanmalka Madame Magdalena C. Maika L. Malen Mandy S. Manolis K. Manon Marc Marcel L. Marco Marco D. Marco D. Marco R. Marco S. Marcos A. Marcus A. Marek Z. Margi A. Margo V. Maria Maria A. Maria G. Mariana R. Marianela C. Marianna R. Marie B. Marie G. Marie L. Marilu Mario Marissa L. Marko Markus D. Marla H. Marlen P. Marlene S. Marlo W. Marnie D. Marta R. Marta S. Marti Martin A. Martin J. Martin M. Martin W. Martine L. Martyna Marwan M. Mary K. Mary L. Mary M. Mary V. Maryam Masha S. Massimo Matan L. Matan P. Matan Y. Mate Mathias U. Matija Z. Matt T. Matteo M. Matthew C. Matthew J. Matthew K. Matthew L. Matthew P. Matthias S. Mattias P. Matty Matus K. Maureen M. Max Max D. Maximilian L. Maxine D. Maya Maz E. Megan D. Megan P. Meghan D. Meghan M. Mei L. Mel S. Melanie L. Melanie S. Melissa Melissa A. Melissa B. Melissa P. Melissa S. Mello W. Melody Melody H. Meng L. Menka S. Menzo G. Merete Y. Messianeal Michael Michael A. Michael B. Michael R. Michael V. Michael Y. Michal B. Michal M. Michelle Michelle B. Michelle F. Michelle H. Michelle W. Michiel V. Miguel A. Miguel D. Mijs V. Mike N. Miki C. Mikie M. Miko A. Mippy Miranda Miranda A. Miriam E. Miriam K. Miriam N. Mirko B. Mirmir Miroslava D. Mitchell B. Miu L. Miyoko S. Mohammed A. Momo Momonoguiko Monica K. Monica W. Monique P. Moniza K. Montse D. Morag O. Moran F. Mordehay A. Moshin Mr. Y. Mrblackkat Mrs J. Muhammad K. Murielle E. My Mythical Naama Naama B. Naama G. Naama K. Naama W. Naama Z. Nadia Nadia F. Nadine Nadine Z. Nancy N. Nancy W. Naomi C. Naomi F. Naor B. Nari O. Nata S. Natalia Natalia R. Natalie Natalie Natalie C. Natalie L. Natalie S. Natalie U. Nataša A. Natasha Natasha C. Nathalie U. Nathan D. Nayan C. Nedjma B. Neena S. Neil H. Neora S. Neysa C. Ng J. Nhung N. Niall H. Nicholas C. Nicholas L. Nicky Nicky R. Nico D. Nicole B. Nicole E. Nicole S. Nicolle H. Niki P. Nikki E. Nikki N. Nina Nir B. Nirit Nitay A. Nitsan B. Nitzan G. Niv S. Noa B. Noa K. Noa N. Noa P. Noa Y. Noagilat Noan Noemi B. Noga Noga M. Nora V. Norman K. Not A. O. Obi-Juan T. Oded R. Odin S. Odin V. Ofri Ohad F. Oksana S. Olaf C. Olga W. Omer R. Omri R. Ondine S. Or G. Oran A. Ori Oria C. Orit B. Oriyan Orly Y. Ortal G. Osher E. Osnat C. Osnat P. Pamela Pamela K. Panda M. Paratruth R. Parisha Patricia C. Patricia D. Patricia P. Patricia R. Patrick C. Patrick O. Patrik Paul Paul C. Paul P. Paula B. Paula I. Paula O. Paulina T. Pedro M. Pedro R. Pedro V. Peggy F. Peggy Z. Pequelord Peter D. Peter H. Peter M. Peter W. Phil I. Philip Y. Philipp Pierpaolo Pippimd Polly M. Prue Puja S. Purrdence Qing Qtym R V. Rabea K. Rachael B. Rachel A. Rachel E. Rachel O. Rachel R. Rachel S. Radoslaw Ragna D. Rainie Rakefet Z. Rallyn T. Rany Raphael Raquel R. Rasadullaev Ratika Ravi R. Raw T. Ray H. Rayhne S. Rebecca F. Rebecca H. Rebecca M. Rebecca N. Rebecca S. Rebecca Y. Rebekah S. Reinis Z. Renae Renata O. Renee Renee L. Reto S. Reut L. Rhonda Rich A. Richard H. Richard O. Richard-Michael C. Ricky C. Ricky F. Rie R. Rik W. Rita Ritta Ro-I B. Rob S. Robbie W. Robert Robert C. Robin Robyn Roca S. Rockway B. Rod Rodney D. Rodrigo O. Roel K. Roi S. Romal G. Roman P. Romina N. Ron N. Ron R. Roni K. Ronny L. Ross W. Rossana V. Rouven Z. Rowan Roxanne Roxanne C. Roy G. Royce Roze Ruby A. Russell Russell M. Ruth B. Ruth G. Ruthie S. Ryan Ryan A. Ryan P. S J. Saar F. Sabrina C. Sachi G. Sagi Sagi I. Sahar H. Sakelarios K. Salena W. Salla T. Samantha Samantha B. Samantha L. Samuel G. Samuel U. Sanchia K. Sander T. Sandra S. Sandro Sandy C. Sandy E. Sangita N. Sanyapong C. Sara Sara C. Sara G. Sara K. Sara M. Sara P. Sara S. Sarah Sarah B. Sarah C. Sarah D. Sarah F. Sarah H. Sarah K. Sarah L. Sarah M. Sarah P. Sarah R. Sarah T. Sarakov W. Sascha R. Sascha W. Savion B. Schechtmann Scott A. Scott B. Scott L. Sean B. Sean P. Sean S. Sebastian Selene Serena Sergey P. Shachar B. Shahar A. Shail M. Shane C. Shani G. Shannon B. Shannon S. Shara T. Sharon L. Sharon D. Sharona R. Shauna B. Shaunda L. Shaunna R. Shawn G. Shawn K. Shawne B. Shay Shay C. Shay K. Shayna H. Sheena L. Shelly M. Sher Sheri-Anne H. Sheridee R. Sherri W. Shir P. Shira R. Shireen Shiri Shiri M. Shirley K. Shirousagi Shlomi T. Siah H. Siân M. Silvana M. Simen M. Simon Simon H. Simone Simone K. Siobhan O. Sissel M. Skye G. Skye L. Skylerparis Smadar A. Sofian A. Soila T. Sole C. Song Sonia C. Sonia D. Sonja H. Sonja M. Sonja S. Sophia P. Sophie G. Sophie P. Sophie R. Sophie S. Soygirl Spencer F. Spencer J. Splinter V. Stacy Stefania Stefanie L. Stefanie M. Stephan W. Stephanie Stephanie R. Stephanie S. Stephen P. Steve F. Steve T. Steven M. Steven N. Steven S. Stevland Suat E. Sue C. Sue-Rae R. Suellen F. Sukum T. Sunfaceback Sunny R. Susan Susan B. Susan H. Susan M. Susan R. Susan W. Suzanna G. Suzanne F. Suzanne P. Suzanne S. Suzie Suzy S. Sven S. Svenja S. Sydney S. Sylvain E. Sytse M. Taib L. Takashi C. Tali G. Tali L. Tali P. Tamar Tamara L. Tamir T. Tania Tanya R. Tara Tara B. Tara H. Tara L. Tara T. Tasha T. Tatiana S. Taylor K. Tea M. Ted Teemu L. Teri C. Terri C. The V. Themis T. Theo K. Thibaut V. Thomas Thomas P. Thorsten P. Thrumugnyr Thuy L. Tiffany H. Tiffany J. Tiffany M. Tim H. Timbo Timothy E. Timv Tina L. Tiny H. Titanking Tj T. Tjarda Tom B. Tom D. Tom W. Tomasz Tomer Y. Tomomi Toni C. Tony S. Torborg Trevor D. Tricia B. Triptaku Trish A. Trisha Trude N. Tsahi L. Tzippi W. Uri M. Uria B. Uschi M. Valerie Valerie C. Valter L. Vanakyra Vanessa B. Vanessa C. Vanessa M. Vanessa R. Varick R. Veerle L. Veganuary C. Vera C. Vera F. Veramartins Vered S. Verena B. Verena G. Veronica K. Veronika Vho Vickie L. Victor Victor G. Victor T. Victoria Victoria Victoria B. Viktor D. Vincent C. Virginia Vivian L. Vivika K. Wade W. Wael J. Wanda Wendy L. Wendy M. Wendy R. Wendy T. Whitney N. Wiebke G. Wilfred Will B. William R. William S. Willie Wilma E. Woochul C. Xavier L. Xavier M. Xavier P. Xopher B. Yaara M. Yael E. Yael G. Yael H. Yaeli Manom Yael M. Yaelle H. Yair W. Yaiza Yanivsky Yehonatan G. Yelarney B. Yi-Han F. Yifat C. Yisrael R. Yoni Yoni H. Yulia Yuval Yvonne Zaina Zarah S. Zhan W. Ziba11 Zifan G. Zimmie S. Zo A. Zoe

REFERENCES

Agency for Toxic Substances and Disease Registry. (1999). Mercury. Retrieved from ATSR website.

American Heart Association. (2016, October). Whole Grains and Fiber. Retrieved from American Heart Association website.

Appel, H. M., & Cocroft, R. B. (2014). Plants Respond to Leaf Vibrations Caused by Insect Herbivore Chewing. Oecologia, 175(4), 1257-1266.

Appleby, P., Roddam, A., Allen, N., & Key, T. (2007). Comparative Fracture Risk in Vegetarians and Nonvegetarians in EPIC-Oxford. European Journal of Clinical Nutrition, 61(12), 1400-1406.

Breidt, Jr. F, McFeeters R, Díaz-Muñiz I. 2007. Fermented Vegetables, p 783-793. In Doyle M, Beuchat L (ed),Food Microbiology: Fundamentals and Frontiers, Third Edition.

Carlsen, M. H., Halvorsen, B. L., Holte, K., Bøhn, S. K., Dragland, S., Sampson, L., ... Willey, C. (2010). The Total Antioxidant Content of More Than 3100 Foods, Beverages, Spices, Herbs and Supplements Used Worldwide. Nutrition Journal, 9(1).

Celiac Disease Foundation. (n.d.). Celiac Disease Symptoms. Retrieved from Celiac Disease Foundation website.

Centers for Disease Control and Prevention. (1998). Recommendations to Prevent and Control Iron Deficiency in the United States. Morbidity and Mortality Weekly Report.

Centers for Disease Control and Prevention. (2015, March 9). Salmonella. Retrieved March 12, 2018, from https://www.cdc.gov/salmonella/general/prevention.html

Centers for Disease Control and Prevention. (2017, November 8). Antibiotic Resistance. Retrieved March 13, 2018, from https://www.cdc.gov/foodsafety/challenges/antibiotic-resistance.html

Chandroo, K., Duncan, I., & Moccia, R. (2004). Can Fish Suffer?: Perspectives on Sentience, Pain, Fear and Stress. Applied Animal Behaviour Science, 86(3-4), 225-250.

Cook, G. (2012). Do Plants Think? Scientific American. Retrieved from Scientific American website.

Dahl, W. J., & Stewart, M. L. (2015). Position of the Academy of Nutrition and Dietetics: Health Implications of Dietary Fiber. Journal of the Academy of Nutrition and Dietetics, 115(11), 1861-1870.

DeBruicker, J. (2011). How much meat do we eat, anyway? Retrieved from Johns Hopkins Center for a Livable Future website: Livable Future blog.

The Economist. (2012). Kings of the carnivores. Retrieved from The Economist website.

Enviromental Working Group. (2011). Meat Eaters Guide to Climate Change and Health. Retrieved from Enviromental Working Group website.

Food and Drug Administration. (2018, January 3). How to Understand and Use the Nutrition Facts Label. Retrieved from FDA website.

Food and Drug Administration. (n.d.). Sodium in Your Diet. Retrieved from FDA website.

Food Standards Agency. (2016). Current EU Approved Additives and Their E Numbers. Retrieved from FSA website.

Harvard. (2017, August 22). How much calcium do you really need? Retrieved from Harvard Health Publishing website.

Harvard. (2017, February 27). Protein. Retrieved from Harvard The Nutrition Source website.

Joint FAO/WHO Expert Consultation on Human Vitamin and Mineral Requirements. (2004). Vitamin and mineral requirements in human nutrition (2nd ed.). Geneva: FAO/WHO.

Katz, S. (2012). The Art of Fermentation: An in-Depth Exploration of Essential Concepts and Processes from Around the World. Philadelphia, Pa: Free Library of Philadelphia.

Kupper, C. (2005). Dietary Guidelines and Implementation for Celiac Disease. Gastroenterology, 128(4), S121-S127.

Kushi, L. H., Byers, T., Doyle, C., Bandera, E. V., McCullough, M., & Gansler, T. (2006). American Cancer Society Guidelines on Nutrition and Physical Activity for Cancer Prevention: Reducing the Risk of Cancer With Healthy Food Choices and Physical Activity. CA: A Cancer Journal for Clinicians, 56(5), 254-281.

Kreider, R. B., Wilborn, C. D., Taylor, L., Campbell, B., Almada, A. L., Collins, R., ... Antonio, J. (2010). ISSN exercise & sport nutrition review: research & recommendations. Journal of the International Society of Sports Nutrition, 7, 7.

Mahan, L. K., In Escott-Stump, S., In Raymond, J. L., & Krause, M. V. (2012). Krause's food & the nutrition care process (13th ed.). St. Louis, MO: Elsevier/Saunders.

Mangels, R., Messina, V., & Messina, M. (2012). The Dietitian's Guide to Vegetarian Diets: Issues and Applications (3rd ed.). Sudbury, Mass: Jones and Bartlett.

Mekonnen, M. M., & Hoekstra, A. Y. (2011). The green, blue and grey water footprint of crops and derived crop products. Hydrology and Earth System Sciences, 15(5), 1577-1600.

Messina, V. (2015). Health Effects of Soy. Academy Of Nutrition And Dietetics.

Mighty Organization. (n.d.). The Ultimate Mystery Meat. Retrieved from Mightyearth website.

National Research Council (US) Committee on Recognition and Alleviation of Pain in Laboratory Animals. (2009). Recognition and Alleviation of Pain in Laboratory Animals. Washington, D.C.: National Academies Press.

Nutrient Data Laboratory (U.S.). (1996). USDA Food Composition Data. Retrieved from website: USDA website

Ogden, L. (2007, April 4). The Environmental Impact of a Meat-Based Diet. Retrieved from Vegetarian Times website.

Orlich, M. J., Singh, P. N., Sabaté, J., Jaceldo-Siegl, K., Fan, J., Knutsen, S., ... Beeson, W. L., & Fraser, G. E. (2013). Vegetarian Dietary Patterns and Mortality in Adventist Health Study 2. JAMA Internal Medicine, 173(13), 1230.

Pimentel, D., & Pimentel, M. (2003). Sustainability of meat-based and plant-based diets and the environment. The American Journal of Clinical Nutrition, 78(3), 660S-663S.

Pimentel, D., Berger, B., Filiberto, D., Newton, M., Wolfe, B., & Nandagopal, S. (2004). Water Resources: Agricultural and Environmental Issues. BioScience, 54(10), 909.

Procter, S. B., & Campbell, C. G. (2014). Position of the Academy of Nutrition and Dietetics: Nutrition and Lifestyle for a Healthy Pregnancy Outcome. Journal of the Academy of Nutrition and Dietetics, 114(7), 1099-1103.

Qi, L., Van Dam, R. M., Rexrode, K., & Hu, F. B. (2006). Heme Iron From Diet as a Risk Factor for Coronary Heart Disease in Women With Type 2 Diabetes. Diabetes Care, 30(1), 101-106.

Ranganathan, J., & Waite, R. (2016, April). Sustainable Diets: What You Need to Know in 12 Charts. Retrieved from World Resources Institute blog.

Scarborough, P., Appleby, P. N., Mizdrak, A., Briggs, A. D., Travis, R. C., Bradbury, K. E., & Key, T. J. (2014). Dietary Greenhouse Gas Emissions of Meat-eaters, Fish-eaters, Vegetarians and Vegans in the UK. Climatic Change, 125(2), 179-192.

Skye Gould, Lauren F Friedman. (2015, September 26). The Countries Where People Eat the Most Meat. Retrieved from Business Insider blog.

Tabuchi, H., Rigby, C., & White, J. (2017, February 24). Amazon Deforestation, Once Tamed, Comes Roaring Back. Retrieved from The New York Times website.

United States Department of Agriculture. (2010). USDA Database for the Oxygen Radical Absorbance Capacity (ORAC) of Selected Foods. Retrieved from U.S. Dept. of Agriculture, Agricultural Research Service, Beltsville Human Nutrition Research Center, Nutrient Data Laboratory website: http://hdl.handle.net/10113/43336

United States Department of Agriculture. (2018, January 4). Food Additive Status List. Retrieved from FDA website.

Venderley, A. M., & Campbell, W. W. (2006). Vegetarian Diets. Sports Medicine, 36(4), 293-305.

Vesanto, M. (n.d.). Smoke Point of Oils. Retrieved from Veghealth website.

Vesanto, M., Winston, C., & Levin, S. (2016). Position of the Academy of Nutrition and Dietetics: Vegetarian Diets. Journal of the Academy of Nutrition and Dietetics, 116(12), 1970-1980.

Warburton, D. E. (2006). Health Benefits of Physical Activity: The Evidence. Canadian Medical Association Journal, 174(6), 801-809.

The World Bank. (2004). Causes of Deforestation of the Brazilian Amazon. Retrieved from The World Bank website.

World Health Organization. (2014). Genetically Modified Food. Retrieved from WHO website.

LOOKIN' FOR SOMETHIN'?

Made in United States
North Haven, CT
09 October 2021